Associate Vice President: Renee Gardner
Editorial Director: Cindy Tripp
Associate Editorial Director: Thomas Super
Project Manager: Jillian McCarthy
Editors: Danielle Curran, Pam Halloran, Kathy Kellman,
Theresa MacVicar, Dawn Nuttall, Lauren Van Wart
Cover Design: Matt Pollock
Cover Illustrator: O'Lamar Gibson
Book Design: Mark Nodland, Timothy Theriault

NOT FOR RESALE

ISBN 978-1-4957-2002-4
©2017–Curriculum Associates, LLC
North Billerica, MA 01862

BTS20

802656

Table of Contents

Unit 1 Numbers 1–5

Standards

Lesson

Standards in boldface are the focus standards that address major lesson content.

Table of Contents   **iii**

Standards in boldface are the focus standards that address major lesson content.

Standards in boldface are the focus standards that address major lesson content.

Table of Contents continued

Standards in boldface are the focus standards that address major lesson content.

Name _____

Understand Counting

Children identify items to count in a picture and in the classroom.
Ask: *What are some objects in the picture that you might count?* Have children
identify and circle some of the things they see that people might count.

Then lead the class on a walk around the classroom. Encourage children to
think about what happens in each area and identify items people might count.

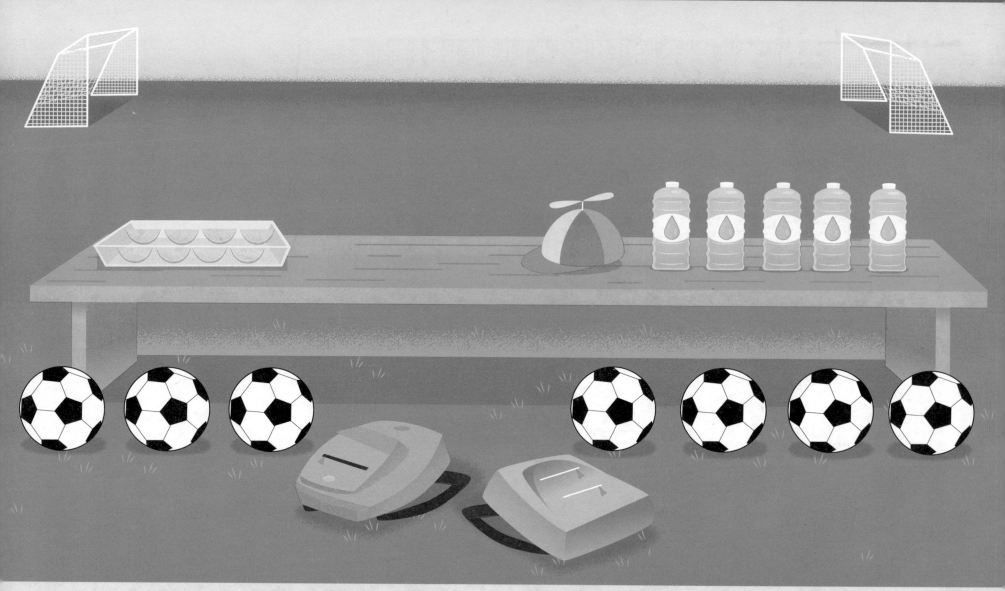

Children identify items to count in a picture and think of other places people might count. Ask what someone might count at a sports field. Then discuss the soccer field scene and have children circle things people might count.

Ask children to think about other places where people might count things and what they might count there. Help children to see people are counting in different places and at different times throughout the day.

Understand Counting

Name _____

Why do we count?

Encourage children to discuss things people might count and why they want to count them. Then ask children to draw a picture of something they have counted or might want to count, such as stickers or other collectibles.

Talk About It What are some other things that you count?

Guide children to match each object to a tile to find the number of objects. Have children draw a line from each object to a number, starting with 1. Ask children to circle the number that tells how many objects.

<u>Talk About It</u> How does drawing a line from each girl to a number help you know how many girls there are?

4   **Lesson 1 • Guided Exploration**

©Curriculum Associates, LLC   Copying is not permitted.

Understand Counting

Name _____

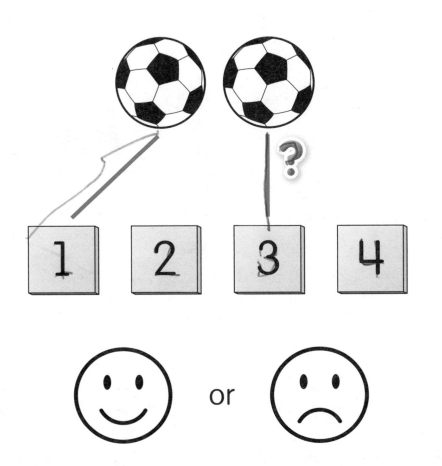

Guide children to discuss whether the objects are counted correctly or not. Have children color the happy face if the objects are counted correctly or the sad face if they are not. Guide children to describe what is wrong.

<u>**Talk About It**</u> What is the mistake in counting the soccer balls? What is the mistake in counting the children?

©Curriculum Associates, LLC   Copying is not permitted.

Guided Practice • Lesson 1   5

Draw. Show how many.

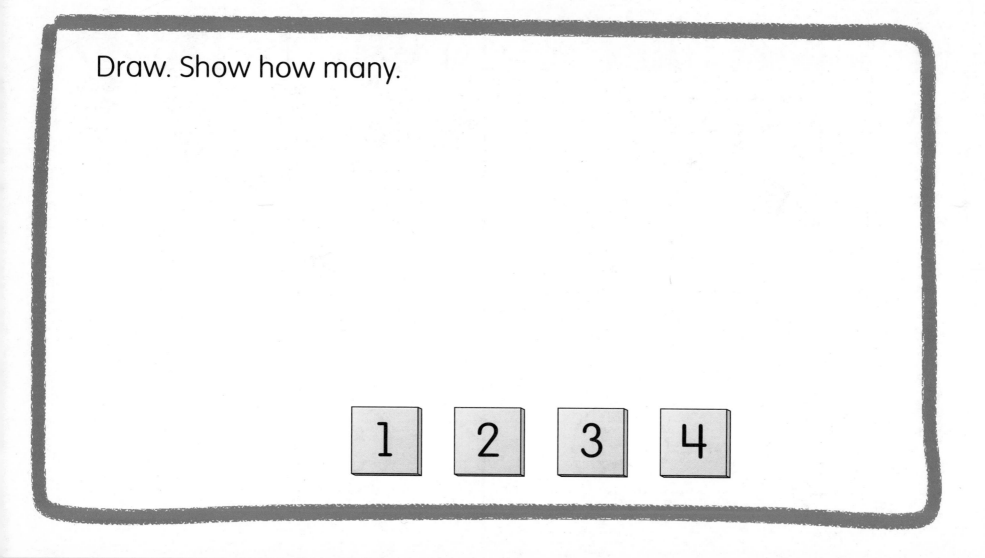

Have children draw something that can be counted with the numbers 1, 2, 3, or 4. Have children draw a line from each object to one number, starting with 1, and circle the last number used to tell how many objects they drew.

<u>Talk About It</u> Work with a partner. Did you draw the same number of objects as other children, or a different number? How can you tell?

6   **Lesson 1 • Independent Practice**

©Curriculum Associates, LLC   Copying is not permitted.

Count 1, 2, and 3

Children make groups of 1, 2, and 3, and practice counting using one-to-one correspondence to find how many are in a group. Introduce the numbers 1, 2, and 3. Discuss activities that 1 child, 2 children, and 3 children might do. Model 1, 2, and 3. Demonstrate counting to show one-to-one correspondence. Then have children draw a picture for 1, 2, and 3.

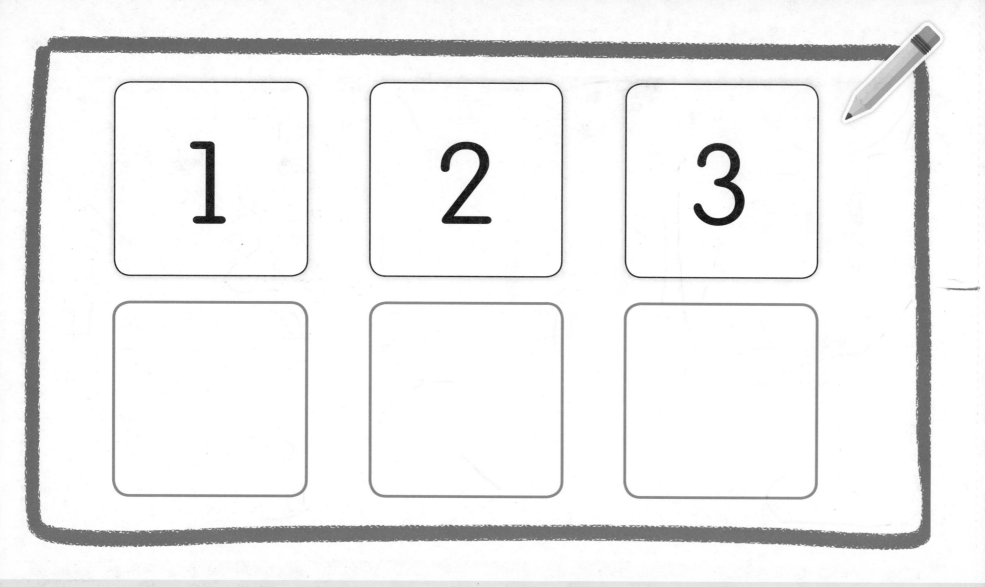

Children use counters, drawings, and fingers to model 1, 2, and 3. Have children place counters in the space below each number to model 1, 2, and 3. Then have children remove the counters and draw dots in the space to show 1, 2, and 3. Point randomly to different cards and ask children to name the number and hold up fingers to show that numbers.

Count 1, 2, and 3

Name _____

Encourage children to describe groups of objects they see in the picture. Ask them to use numbers 1, 2, and 3 as well as words that describe color, size, or position. Guide children to circle any groups of 3 they identify.

Talk About It If you were going to put hats in this picture, how many would you draw? Why?

Practice Together
Count 1, 2, and 3

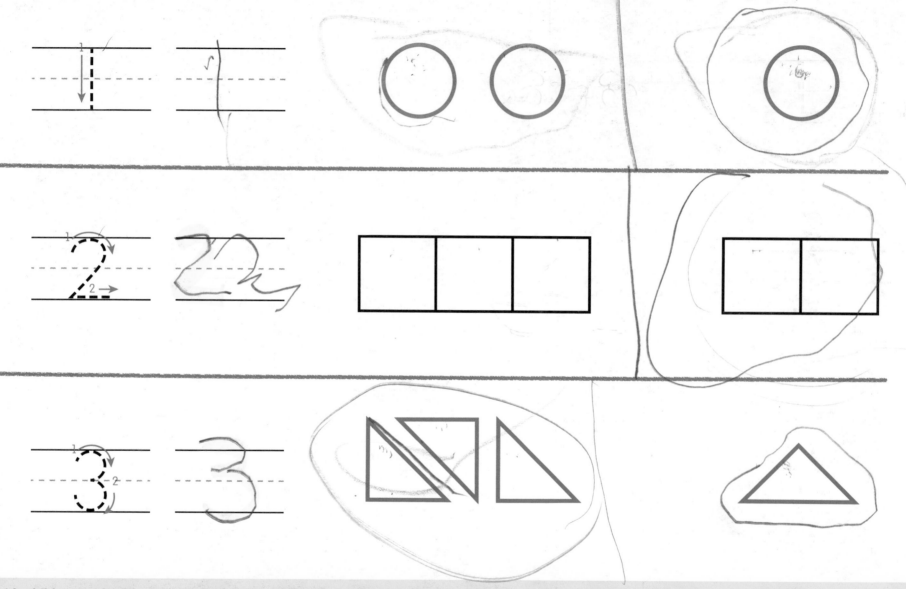

Guide children to identify 1, 2, or 3 shapes and write these numbers. Have children trace and write the given number. Then guide children to color the group that has that number of shapes.

Talk About It   Which pictures show 2? How are the pictures of 2 different?

Count 1, 2, and 3

Name _____

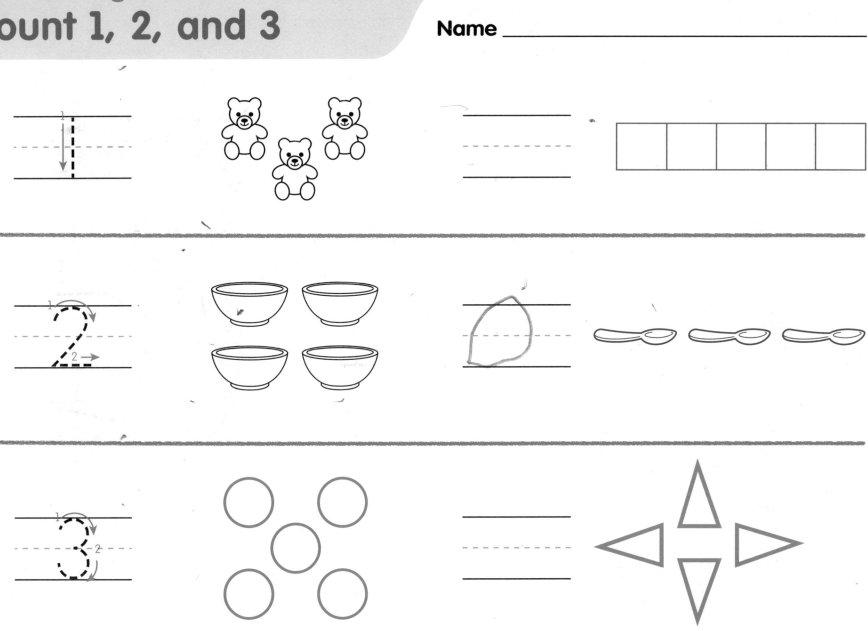

Guide children to color shapes to show counting out. Children count out and practice writing 1 in the top row, 2 in the middle row, and 3 in the bottom row.

<u>Talk About It</u> Work with a partner. Did you both color the same bowls? If you color different bowls, can you both be right?

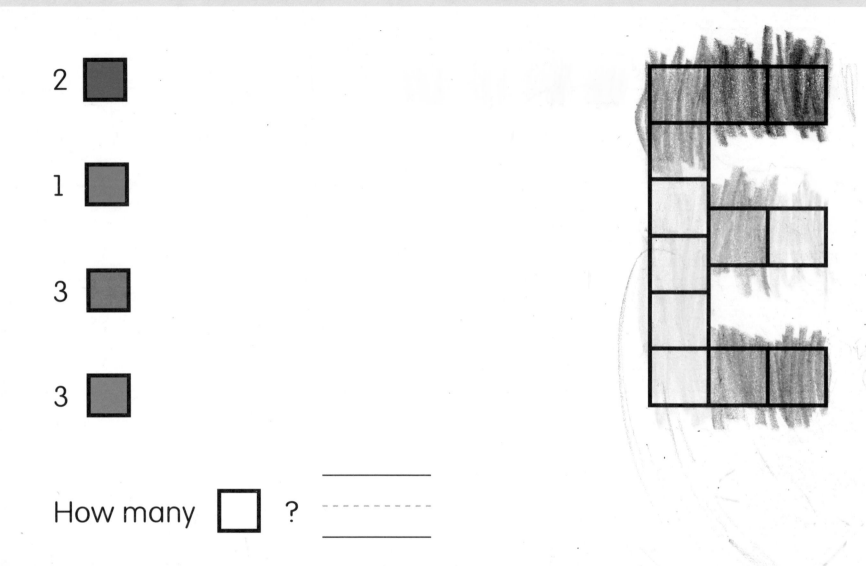

2 ▪

1 ▪

3 ▪

3 ▪

How many ☐ ? _____
- - - - - - - - - -
_____

Have children choose independently which squares to color in the given pattern. Have children color 2 squares blue, 1 green, 3 red, and 3 purple. Have children count the number of white squares and write this number.

Talk About It Work with a partner. Which squares did you color blue? How did you decide which ones to color blue?

12   Lesson 2 • Independent Practice

©Curriculum Associates, LLC   Copying is not permitted.

Count 4

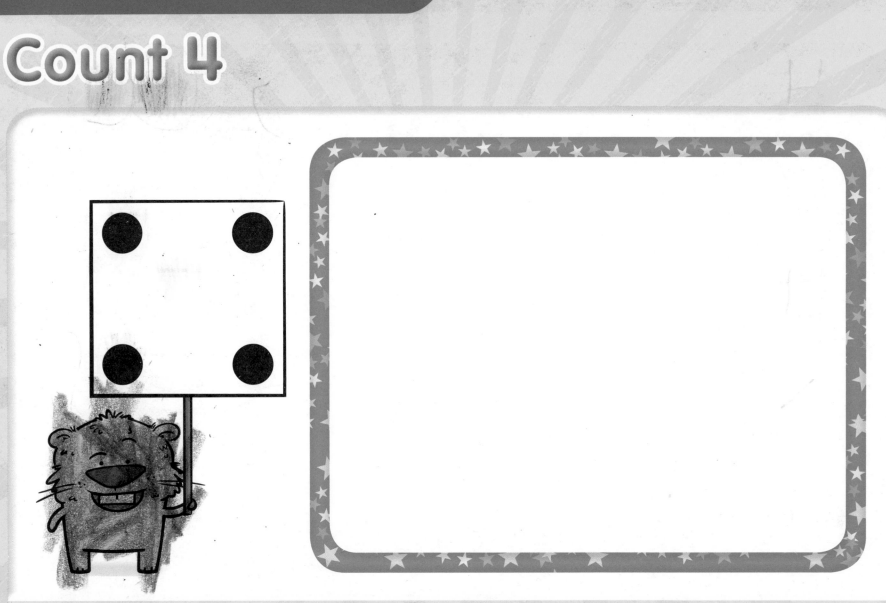

Children explore different arrangements of 4 using counters. Review 1, 2, and 3 using dot cards. Introduce 4 using the dot card. Give children counters and have them arrange the counters as shown on the dot card. Then have children use the counters to show 4 in different arrangements.

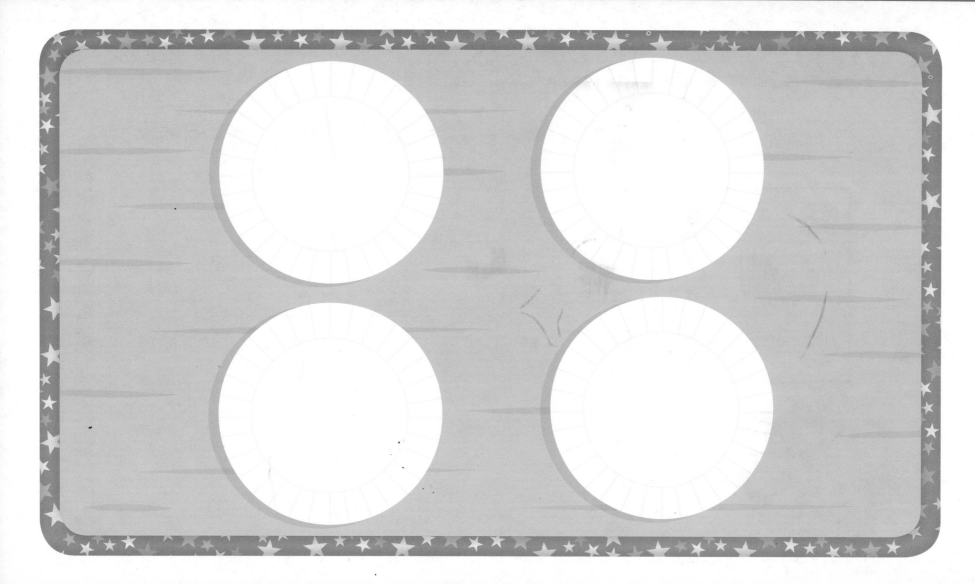

Children count groups of 4 and use a dot card arrangement as a standard for finding groups of 4. Have children count 4 objects. Arrange 4 paper plates to look like the dot card for 4. Place 1 apple (or other object) on each plate and ask: *How many apples are there? How do you know?* Lead the class in discussion. Have students place 1 counter on each of the the plates on their workmat and count the number of counters. Repeat with other objects.

Name _____

Encourage children to describe the groups of objects they see in the picture. Ask children to describe the groups based on the color, size, position, or total number of objects. Have children circle groups of 4 related objects.

<u>Talk About It</u> Do you think the flowers show 4? What are some different ways someone might count the flowers?

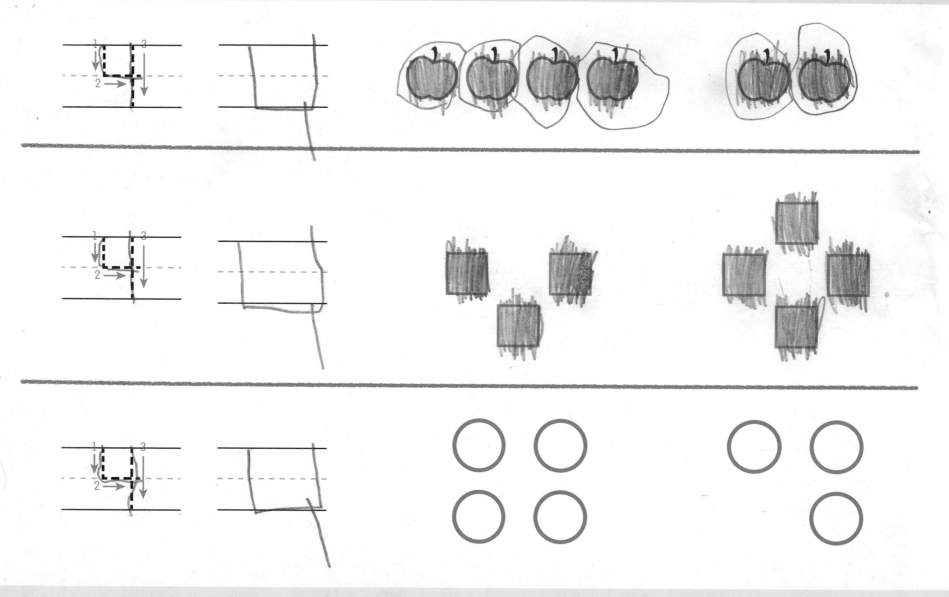

Guide children to trace and write the number 4, then find the groups of 4. Ask children to identify which group of objects shows 4. Have children color the group of 4 in each problem.

Talk About It Which pictures show 3? How are the pictures of 3 different from the pictures of 4?

Count 5

Children explore groups of 5. Pose the problem: *It is Jinya's birthday. He is 5 years old. What are some different ways to place 5 candles on his cake?* Display a dot card for 4 and say: *This is how many candles were on Jinya's cake last year.* Ask children how they can show 5 candles on the dot card "cake." Then have children use the "cake" workmat and counters to show different ways to place 5 candles on a "cake."

Children count groups of 5 and use counters as a standard for finding groups of 5. Give each child 5 crayons and ask: *How many crayons are there?* Have children make different groups of 5 by arranging the crayons in different ways. Then give children 5 counters. Have children practice one-to-one correspondence by gathering groups of 5 objects in the classroom and placing one counter on each object to verify.

Compare Within 5

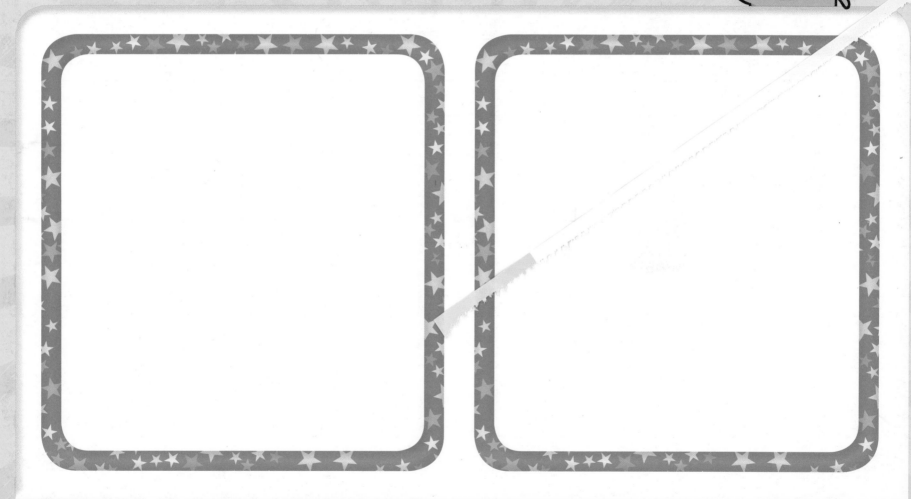

Children discuss ways to find out if two children have the same number of snacks or if one has more. Then they compare groups of counters. Give a child 3 snacks and another child 2 snacks. Ask: *How do we know if both* *children got the same?* Discuss ways to compare. Pair children and give each child 1 to 5 counters. Have each child place his or her counters on one of the workmats, then compare who has more.

Children compare groups of counters to find if they are the same or one has more. Hold up 1 snack in one hand and 3 snacks in the other hand. Have children use counters to model. Ask: *Which hand has more? How do you know?*

Then hold up 2 snacks in each hand. Have children model with counters and compare.

Name _____

Encourage children to talk about the number of objects of various types. Ask children to make comparison statements using *more*, *less*, *fewer*, or *the same*. Have them draw lines from each plate to one cup to compare those groups.

Talk About It   Do you think there are more than 3 people coming to this party? Why or why not?

Compare Within 5

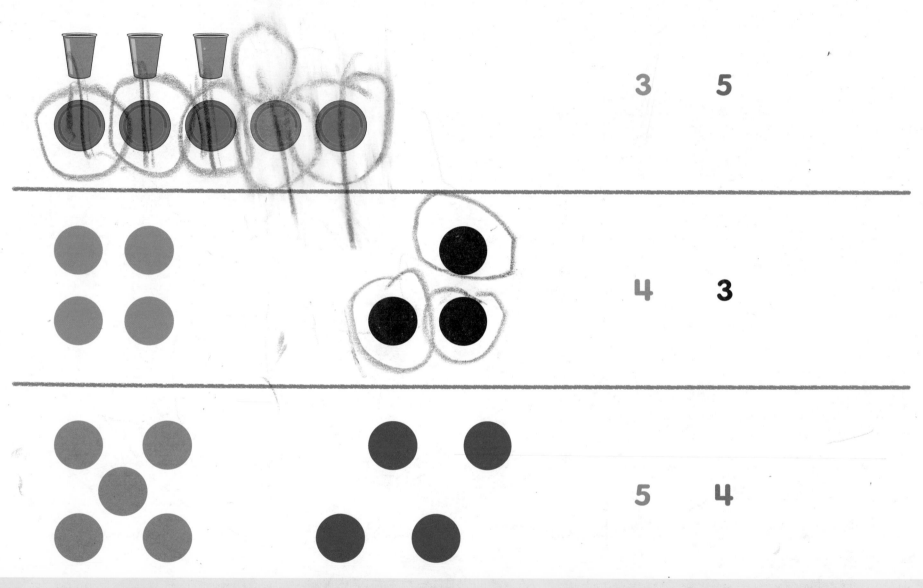

		3	5
		4	3
		5	4

Guide children to compare two groups of objects and circle the group with more.
Have children circle the number that is more. For each problem, ask children to discuss how they can tell which group has more.

Compare Within 5

Name _____

Which is less?

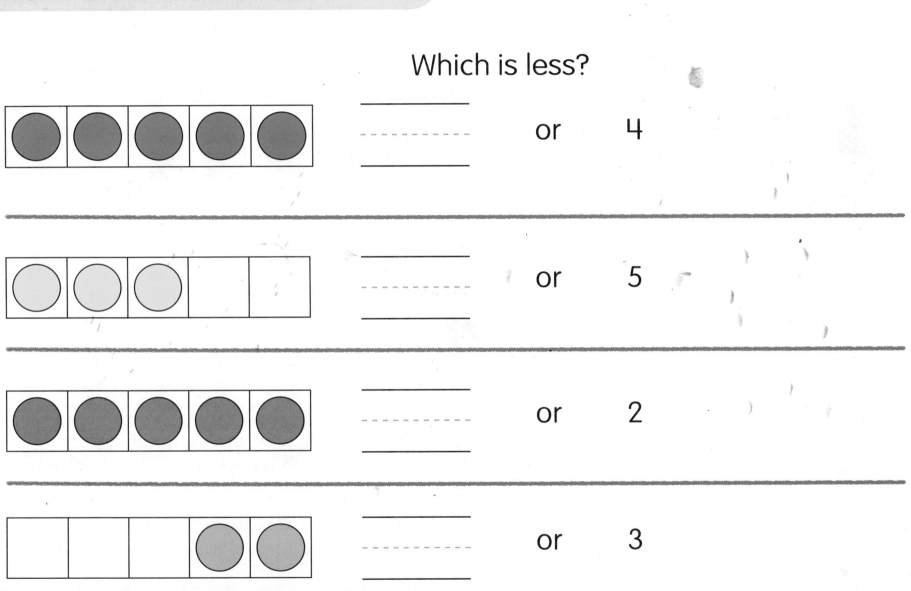

_____ or 4

_____ or 5

_____ or 2

_____ or 3

Guide children to count and write how many counters are shown. Ask them to compare that number to the number printed and circle the one that is less. For each problem, ask children to discuss how they can tell which is less.

Talk About It Look at each group of counters. Which group of counters has less than any of the others? How can you be sure?

Draw more.

Draw less.

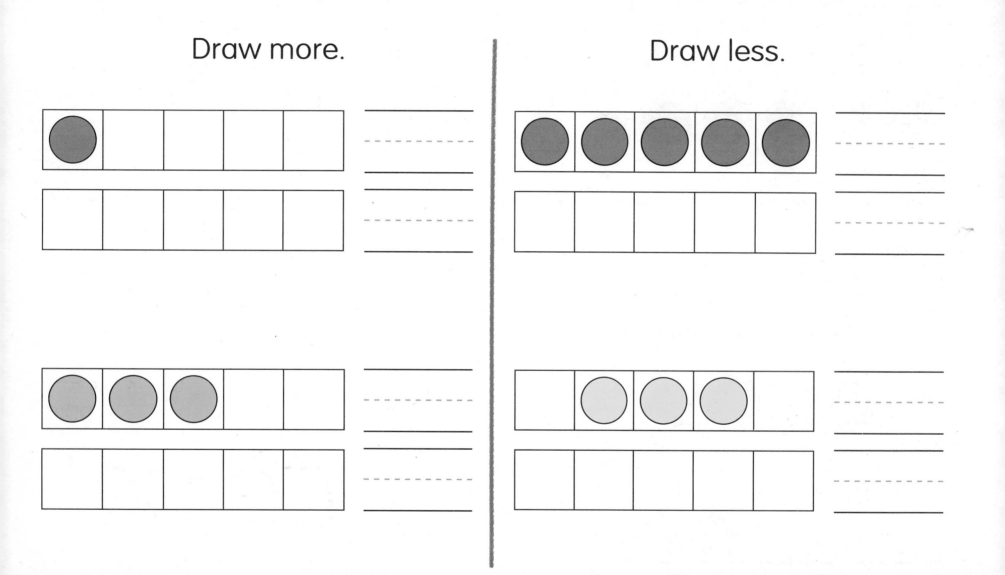

Have children draw more than or less than the number shown in a group of counters.
Have children count and write the given number of counters. Allow children to decide how many counters to draw to show more (on the left) or less (on the right).

<u>**Talk About It**</u> How can you be sure you drew more? How can you be sure you drew less?

Name _____

Make 3, 4, and 5

Children explore different ways to make 5 using two different colored subgroups. Pose the problem: *You want to buy 5 apples. You want some red apples and some yellow apples. Let's make different combinations of red and* *yellow apples.* Invite children to the front of the class to model combinations of 5 as red apples and yellow apples using colored paper. Then have children model different combinations of 5 using two-color counters on the workmat.

Children model problems using counters. Pose another problem: *I have 2 red apples. How many yellow apples should I buy to have 5 apples?*

Then have children use counters to solve the problem. Pose more problems starting with 1, 3, and 4 red apples. Have children use counters to solve.

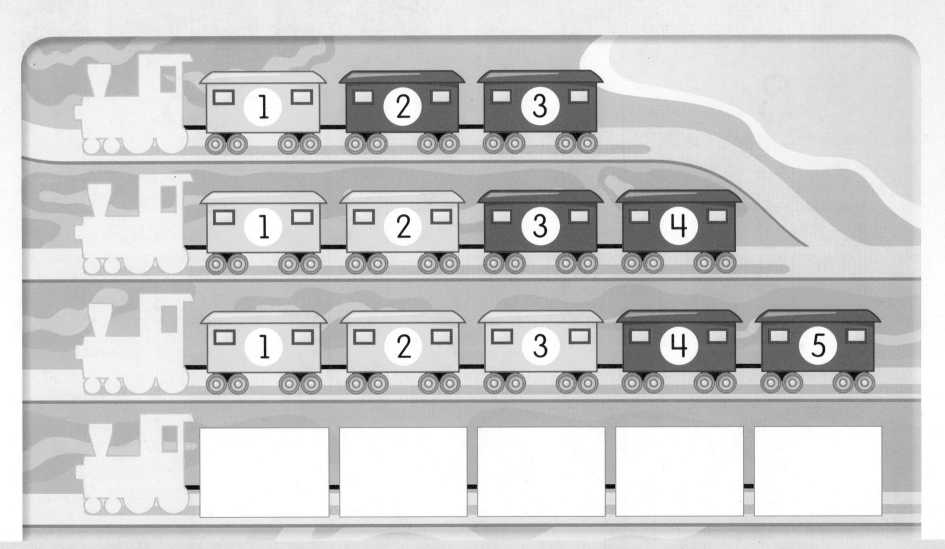

Encourage children to talk about each train. Ask how many cars each train has, how many are yellow, and how many are blue. Discuss any patterns they may see. Have children use yellow and blue crayons to show another way to make a train with 5 cars.

<u>Talk About It</u> What is the same about each group of train cars? What is different?

Make 3, 4, and 5

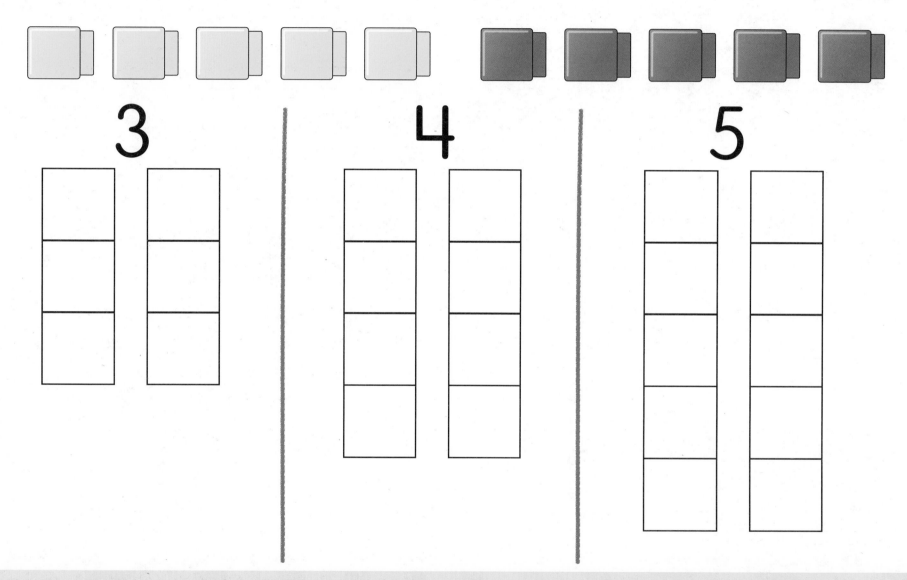

Guide children to build cube trains of 3, 4, and 5, then record their work by coloring the boxes. Model one way to make a train of 3, then have children make 3 a different way. Guide children to also show two ways to make 4 and 5.

Talk About It Work with a partner. Tell how many of each color you used to build 3. Did you use the same number of each color? Did you use the same number of cubes?

Practice Together
Make 3, 4, and 5

Name _____

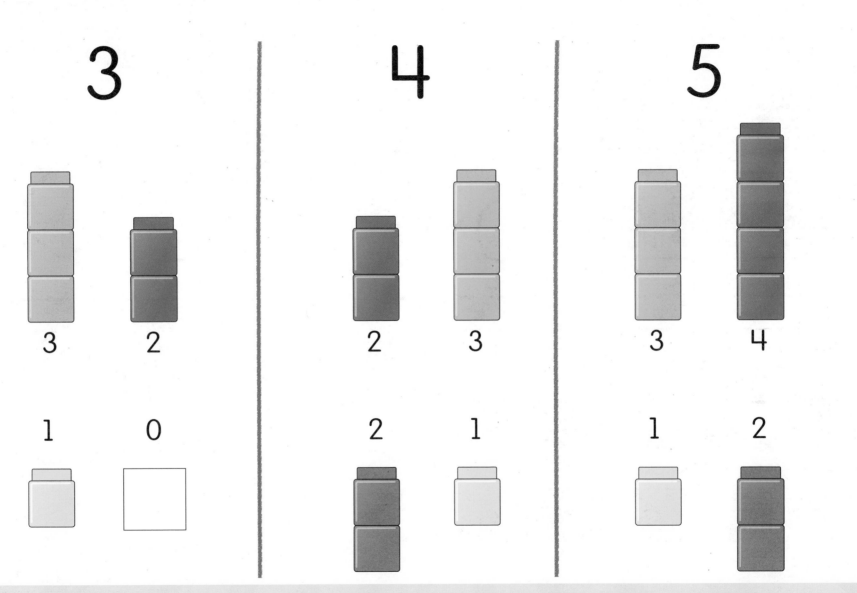

3

3   2

1   0

4

2   3

2   1

5

3   4

1   2

Guide children to match the pieces in the top to the pieces in the bottom to make trains of 3, 4, and 5. Discuss how many of each color were used, and model other number pairs to make each target number.

<u>Talk About It</u> Can you think of other ways to make 4?

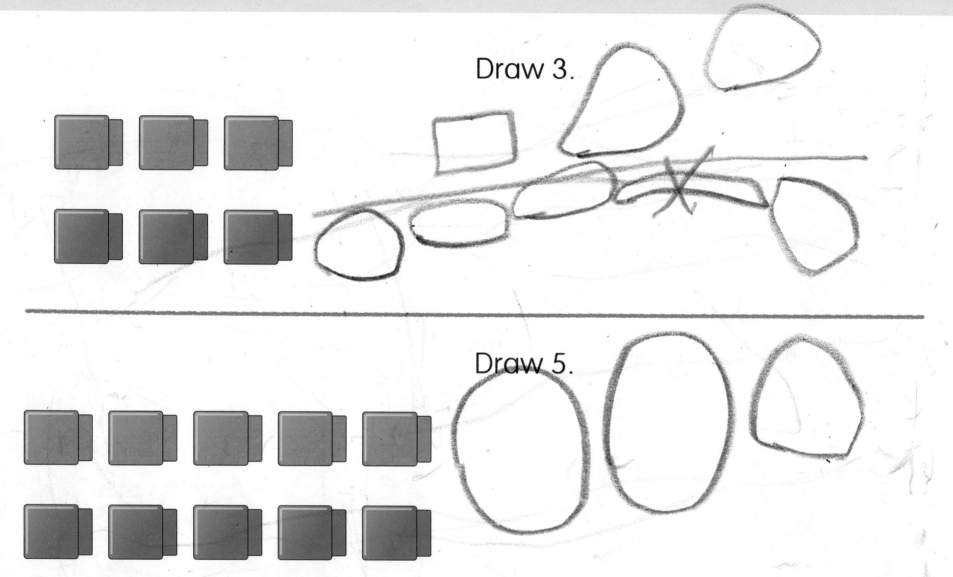

Draw 3.

Draw 5.

Have children use only red and blue cubes to make trains with 3 cubes and then 5 cubes, and then, using only red and blue cubes, draw a picture to show their trains. Develop children's problem-solving skills by allowing them to decide how many of each color to use.

<u>Talk About It</u> How many of each color did you use to build 5? Are there other ways you could build 5 using different numbers of red and blue cubes?

Name _____

Count 6 and 7

Children form groups of 6 and show different arrangements for 6. Review numbers 1 to 5 using dot cards, then display the dot card for 6. Give 6 children paper plates and have them use the plates to make an arrangement of 6 on the floor. Repeat, having other groups of 6 children make different arrangements. Then have children use counters to make arrangements of 6 on the workmat, counting to confirm that each arrangement shows 6.

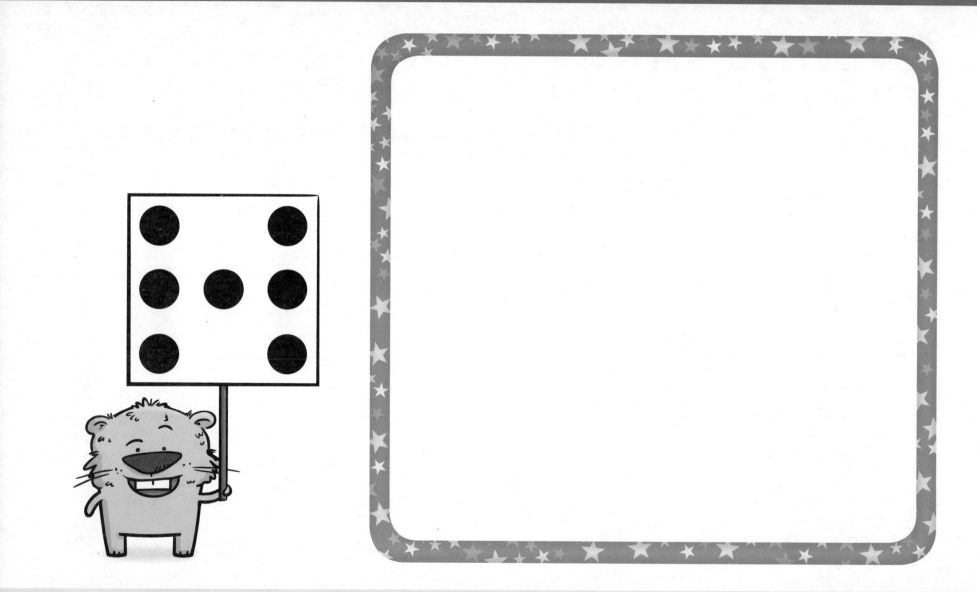

Children form groups of 7 and show different arrangements for 7. Display a dot card for 7. Ask: *How many plates are needed to show the number?* Have groups of 7 use paper plates to make arrangements of 7. Have children show different arrangements of 7 on the workmat using counters. Have children count to verify that each arrangement has 7. Then pairs of children practice identifying the number 6 or 7 on dot cards by counting.

Encourage children to describe the groups of objects they see in the picture. Ask children to find groups of 6 related objects and groups of 7 related objects. Have children circle a group of 6 with one color and a group of 7 with another color.

Talk About It What are some different ways you can count the windows in the tan building?

Count 6 and 7

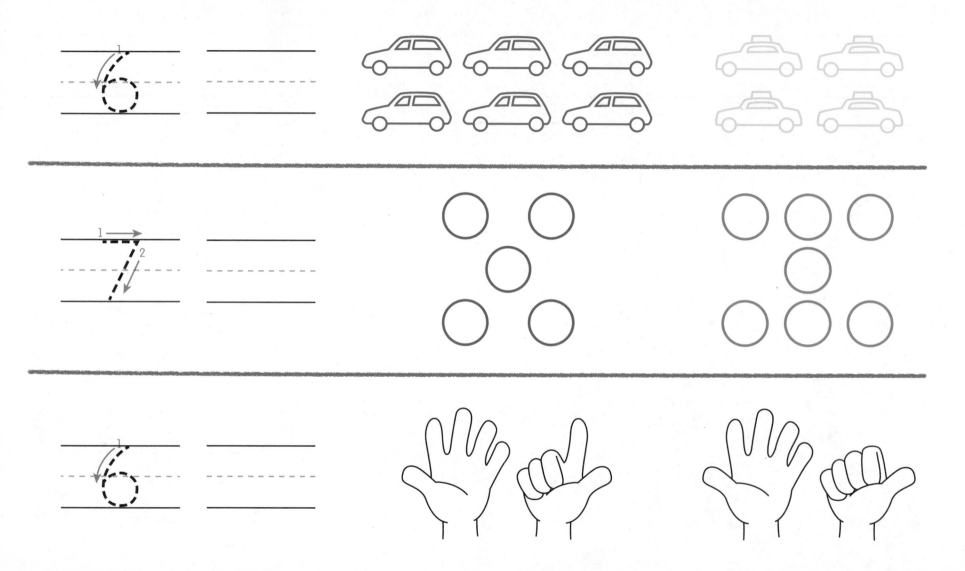

Guide children to find the group that shows 6 or 7. Have children trace and write the number at the beginning of each problem. Have children color the group with the correct number of objects.

Talk About It Look at the pictures of the blue cars and the yellow taxis. How are they different? How are they alike?

40 Lesson 7 • Guided Practice

©Curriculum Associates, LLC Copying is not permitted.

Count 6 and 7

Name _____

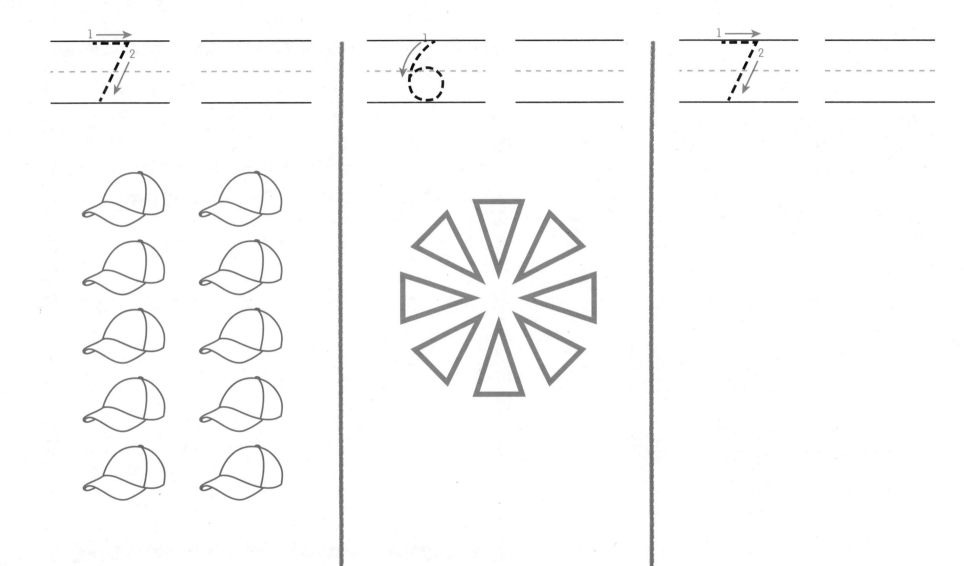

Guide children to count out and color 6 or 7 objects. In the first two problems, have children trace and write the number, then color that many shapes. In the last problem, ask children to trace and write 7 and then draw a picture to show 7 of something.

<u>Talk About It</u> Work with a partner. Did you and your partner color the same 7 hats? How many hats are not colored?

©Curriculum Associates, LLC   Copying is not permitted.

Guided Practice • Lesson 7   41

Count 6 and 7

How many children? _____

Draw 1 🍎 for each child.

Have children count and write the number of children pictured, then draw 1 apple for each child pictured. Allow children to find their own strategies for figuring out how many apples to draw.

<u>Talk About It</u>   How did you decide how many apples to draw?

Make 6 and 7

Children explore different ways to make 6. Pose the problem: *6 muffins fit in a box. How can you fill the box with banana muffins and blueberry muffins?* Have children act out combinations of 6 banana and blueberry muffins using blue and yellow paper. Then have children explore other combinations of 6 using yellow and blue connecting cubes to represent the muffins. Have children use one side for blue cubes and the other for yellow cubes.

Children compose groups of 6 starting from a given number. Display 5 yellow connecting cubes and pose another problem. Say: *I have 5 banana muffins. How many blueberry muffins do I need to have a total of 6 muffins?*

Have children use yellow and blue connecting cubes to verify their answer. Repeat with similar problems, starting with 2, 3, and 4 banana muffins.

Name _____

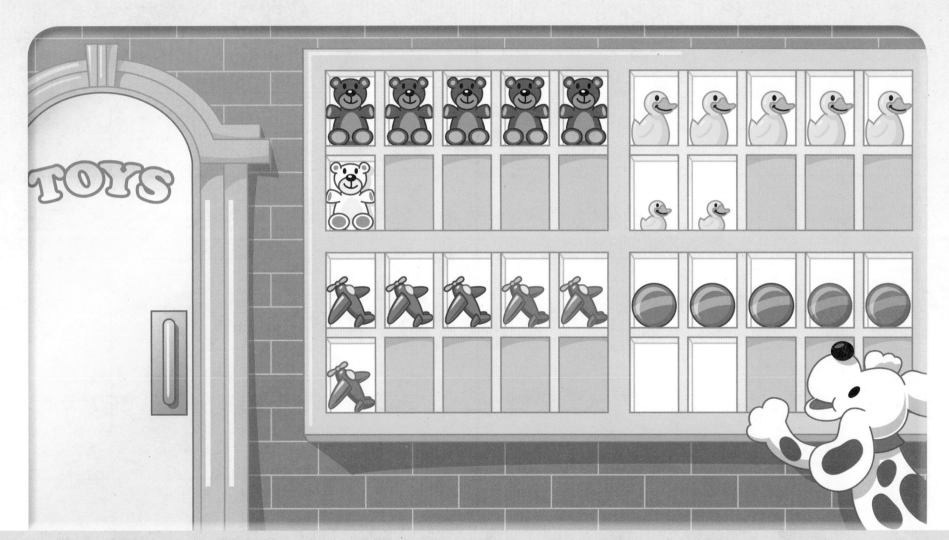

Encourage children to describe the number of each type of toy as the total of two lesser numbers. Have children draw more red balls to make a total of 7. Discuss what is the same and what is different about both groups of 6 and both groups of 7.

Talk About It If 6 children go to this toy store, can every child get a bear? Can every child get a brown bear? How do you know?

Practice Together
Make 6 and 7

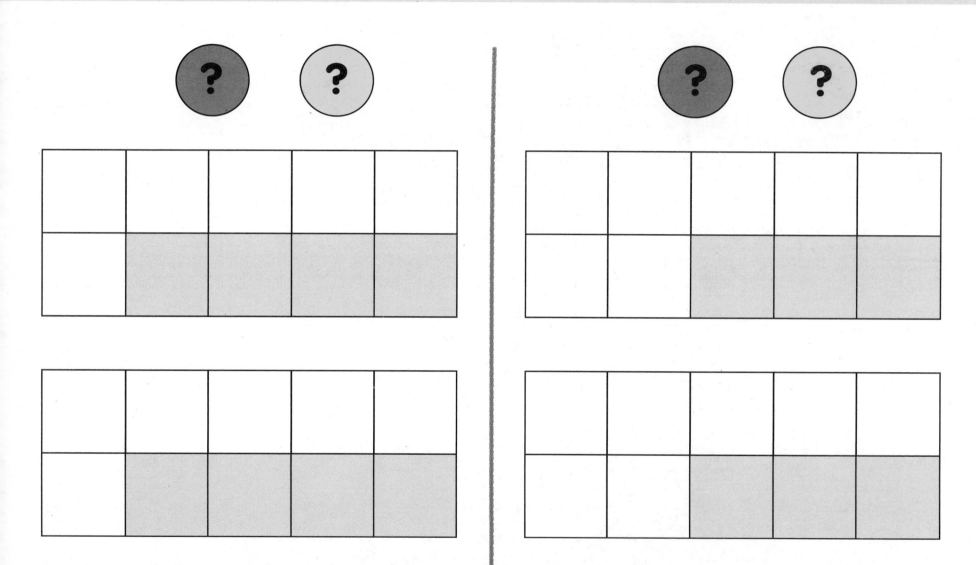

Guide children to use red and yellow counters to make totals of 6 and totals of 7, then **record their work.** Encourage children to keep like-colored counters together. Be sure children understand there is more than one correct solution.

Talk About It Can you make 7 using the same number of red counters and yellow counters? How can you be sure?

Name _____

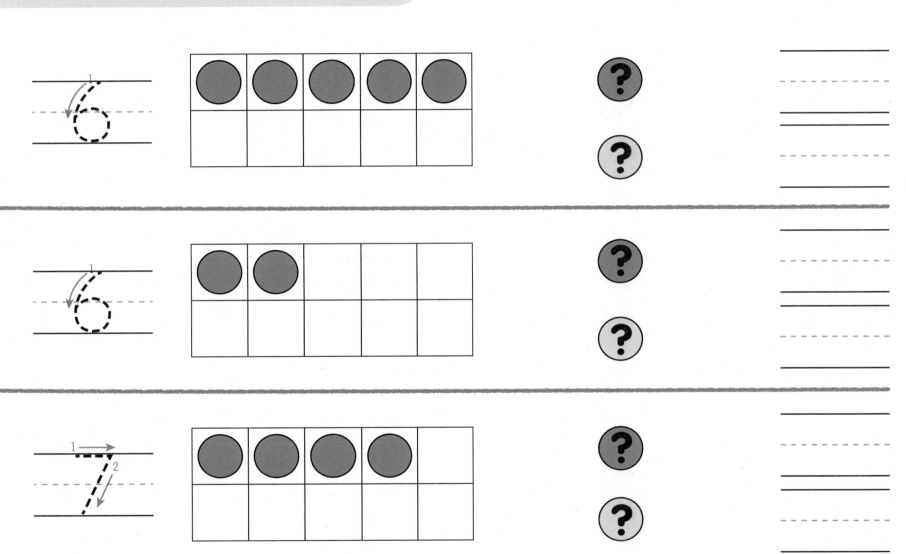

Guide children to complete 10-frames using blue and yellow counters to show 6 or 7.
Have children count and write the number of blue counters and yellow counters they used to make the total.

<u>Talk About It</u> How can you tell how many counters you need to draw to finish each picture so that it shows 6?

©Curriculum Associates, LLC   Copying is not permitted.

Guided Practice • Lesson 8   47

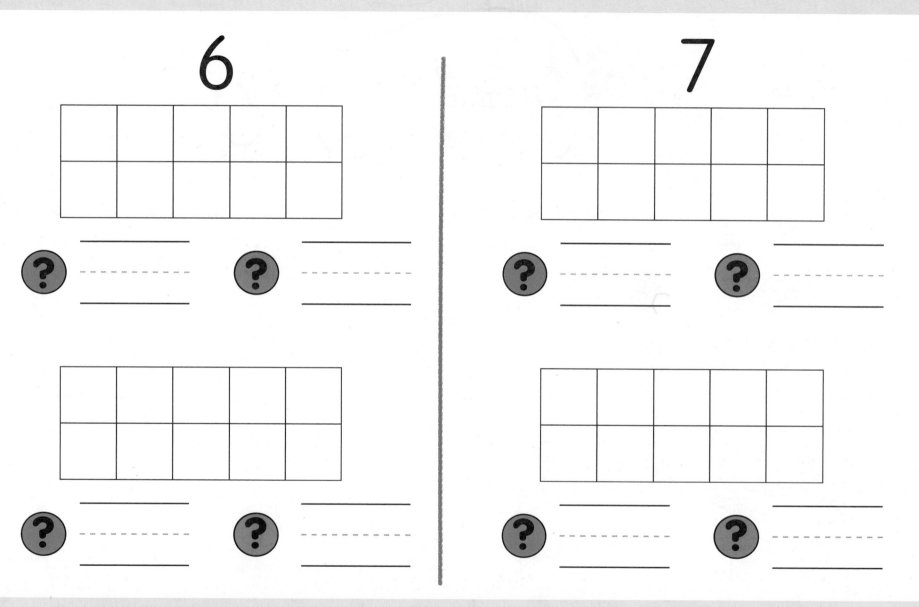

6

7

Have children draw blue and red counters to make a total of 6 in two different ways, and then do the same for 7. Have children count and write the number of red and blue counters in each 10-frame. Allow children to persevere in finding solutions.

Talk About It Work with a partner. Are any of the ways you made 6 the same? Are any of the ways different? How can you tell if all the ways are right?

Name _____

Count 8 and 9

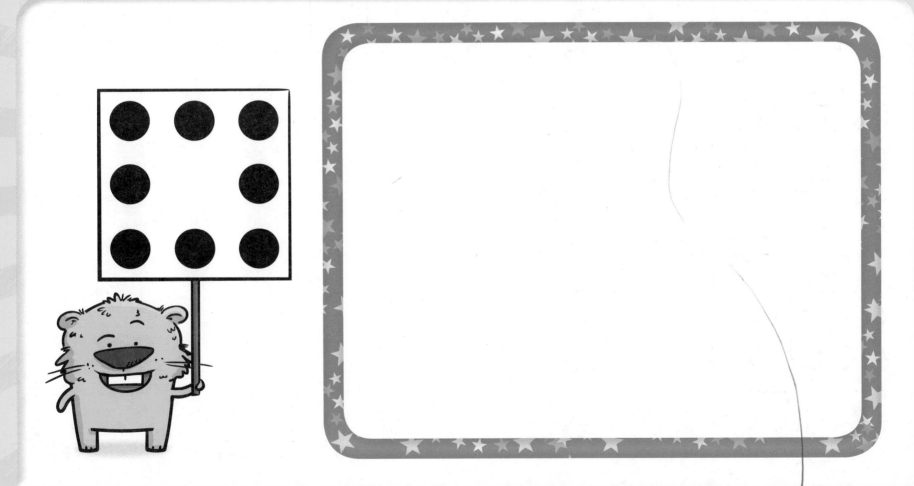

Children compare dot cards 1 to 8, form groups of 8 children, and show different arrangements of 8. Review numbers 1 to 7 using dot cards. Give 8 children paper plates and have them come to the front of the class to make an arrangement of 8. Repeat, having other groups of 8 children make different arrangements. Then have children use counters to make arrangements of 8 on the workmat, counting to confirm that each arrangement shows 8.

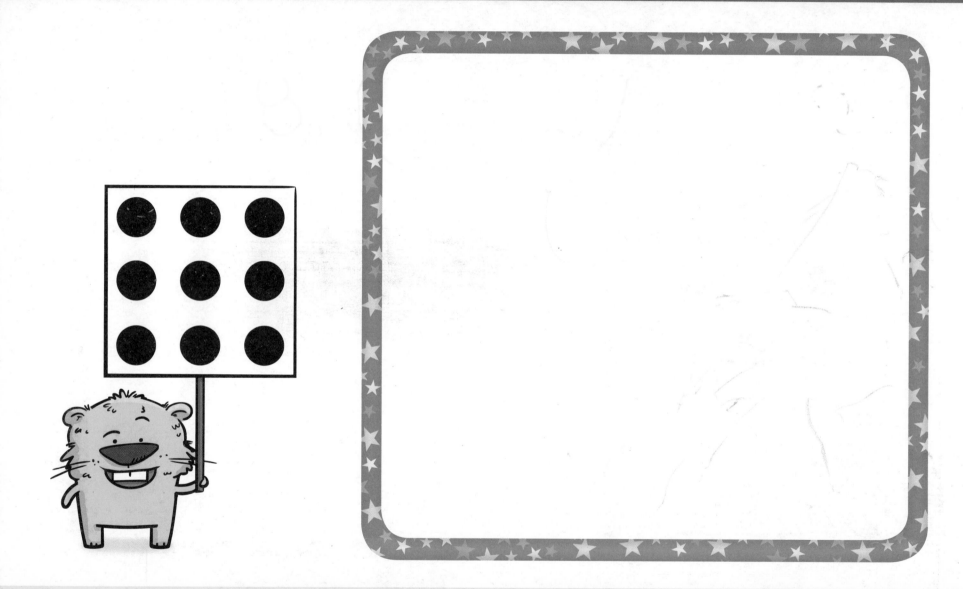

Children form groups of 9 and show different arrangements for 9. Display a dot card for 9. Ask: *How many plates are needed to show the number?* Have a group of 9 children use paper plates to make arrangements of 9. Then have children use counters to show arrangements of 9 on the workmat, counting to verify that each arrangement has 9. Pairs of children practice identifying the number shown on dot cards for 8 and 9 by counting and telling how many.

Name _Yasin_

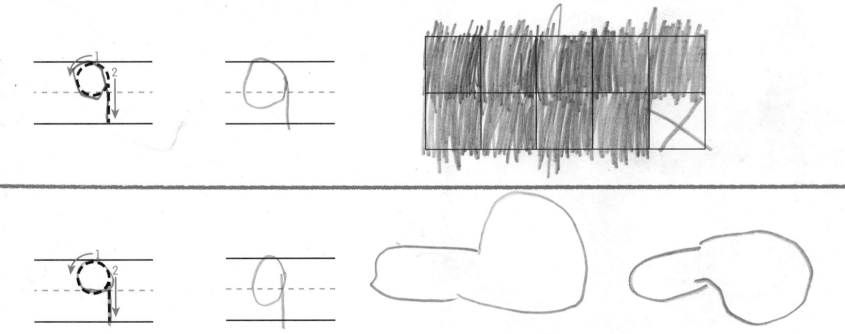

Guide children to count out and color 8 or 9 objects. In the first two problems, have children trace and write the number, then color that many shapes. In the last problem, ask children to trace and write 9 and then draw a picture to show 9 of something.

<u>Talk About It</u> Work with a partner. Look at your drawings in the last problem. How can you check that you both drew 9 objects correctly?

Yasin

How many children? ____

Draw 1 🍃 for each child.

Have children count and write the number of children pictured, then draw one leaf for each child pictured. Allow children to find their own strategies for figuring out how many leaves to draw.

Talk About It How did you figure out how many leaves to draw?

Make 8 and 9

Children explore ways to make 9 using groups of children and two colors of connecting cubes. Pose the problem: *Let's see how many ways you can make 9.* Invite children to act out combinations of 9 by having some children in a row of 9 sit and some stand. Then have children explore combinations of 9 with a partner using connecting cubes. Encourage children to count each combination to verify.

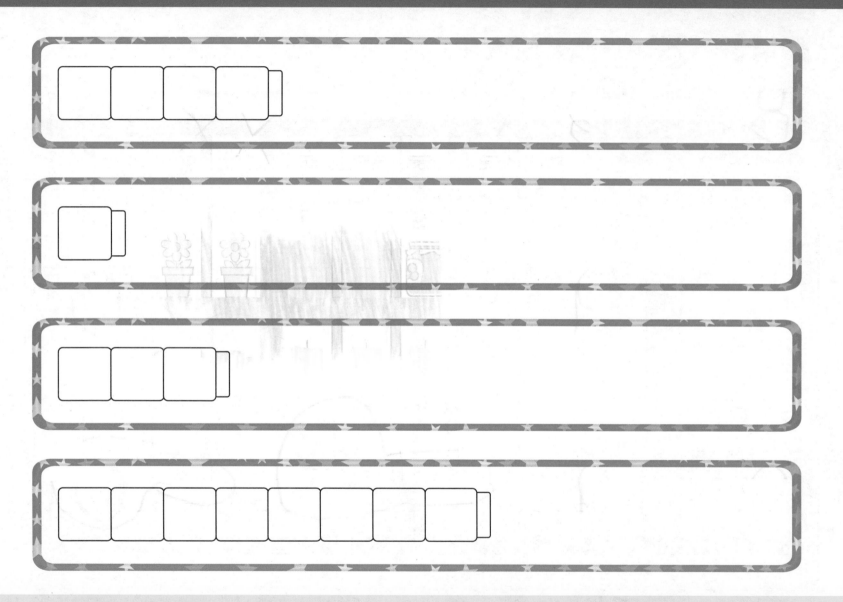

Children make combinations of 9 starting from a given number. Pose a problem. Invite 4 children to the front of the room and ask: *How many more children do I need to have 9 children?* Have children model the problem using connecting cubes. Repeat, starting with 1, 3, and 8 children.

Name _____

Encourage children to use numbers to describe each group of gifts, for example: 8 jars of jam, 5 red and 3 blue. Note that the cup shelves are not full. How could you show 9 cups? After discussion, have children draw 1 more to make a total of 9 cups.

Talk About It Are there more jars of jam or more candles, or is it the same number? How do you know?

Make 8 and 9

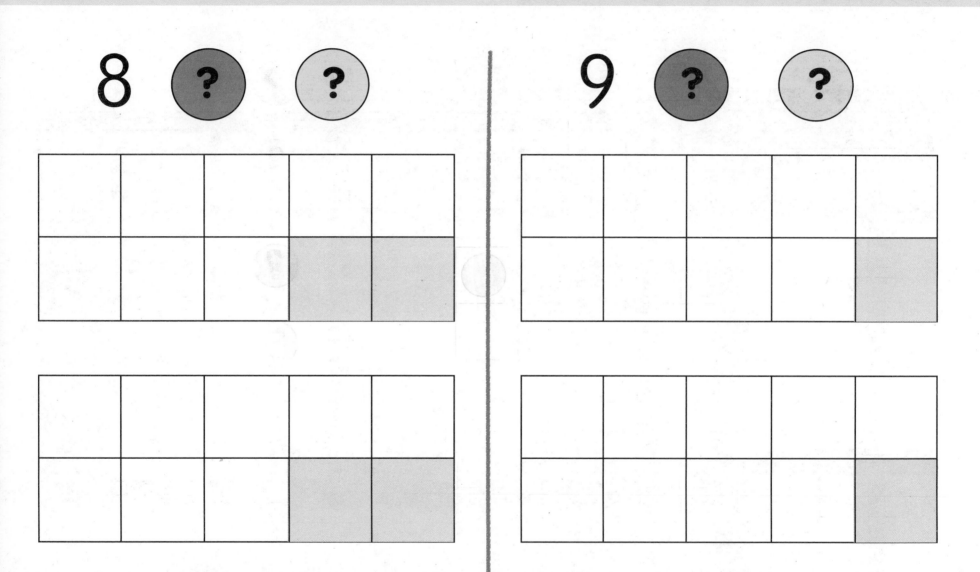

Guide children to make 8 and then 9 using counters on 10-frames. Have children keep like-colored counters together to show two numbers. Have children color counters on the 10-frame to show two different ways to make each number.

<u>**Talk About It**</u> Can you make 9 using the same number of red counters and yellow counters? How can you be sure?

Name _____

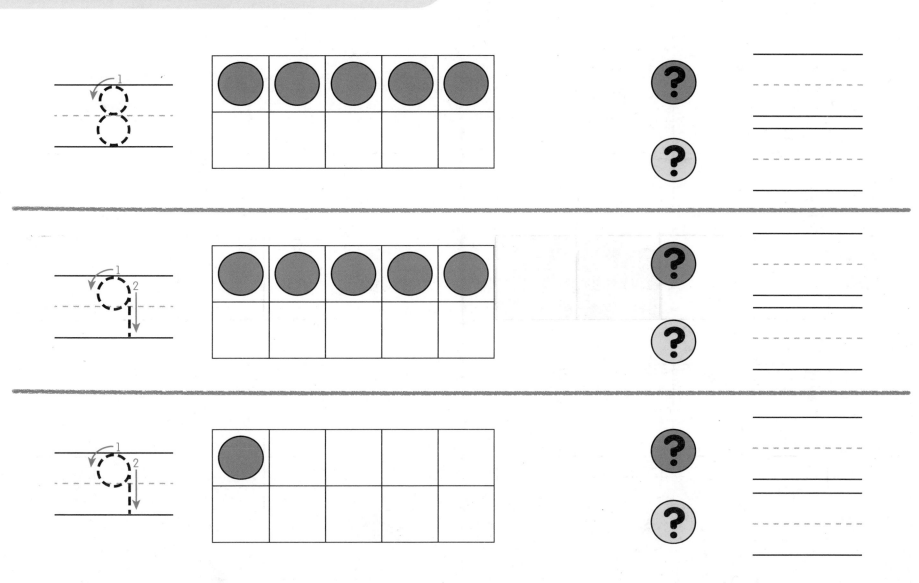

Guide children to complete each 10-frame so it shows 8 or 9. Have children trace the number and then complete the 10-frame. Guide children to count and write the number of blue counters and the number of yellow counters.

Talk About It   Can you make 8 using the same number of blue counters and yellow counters? How do you know?

Make 8 and 9

Make 8.

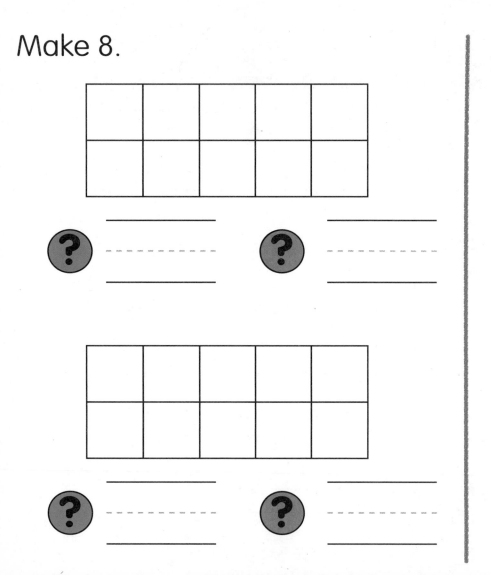

Make 9.

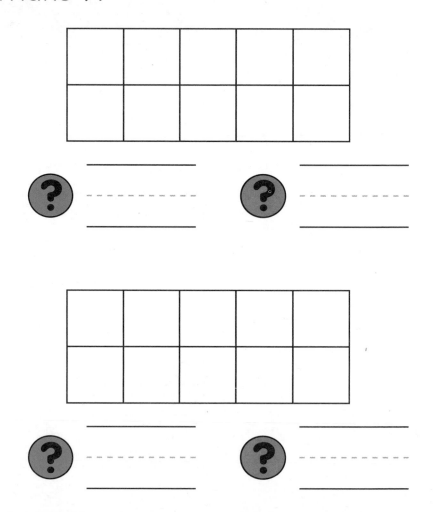

Have children make 8 and make 9 in two different ways using counters on a 10-frame. Have children count and write the number of each color they use. Allow children to persevere in thinking about the different possibilities on their own.

<u>Talk About It</u> Work with a partner. Compare the ways you made 8. Are any of the ways you made 8 the same? Are any of the ways different? How can you tell if all the ways are right?

Name _____

Count 10

Children explore visual images of 10. Children place 5 counters in a column of the 10-frame. Then they add counters one at a time to fill the frame, counting to verify each time. Next they move the counters to be around the edge of the circle. Ask: *How do you count objects in a circle?*

Children explore counting 10 objects shown in different arrangements.
Count out 2 groups of 5 children. Have children identify how many children in each group, then join the groups and have children tell how many in all.

Give each child 5 counters to place on the workmat, then give each child 5 more counters. Discuss the arrangements children used to identify how many counters in all.

Explore Together
Count 10

Name _____

Encourage children to describe groups of 10 they find in the picture. Discuss other size groups as well and note number pairs for 10, such as 3 big rocks and 7 small ones. Have children circle groups of 10.

<u>Talk About It</u> Work with a partner. Look at the bubbles. Do you see a group of 6 bubbles? Where? Do you see a group of 4? Compare your answers.

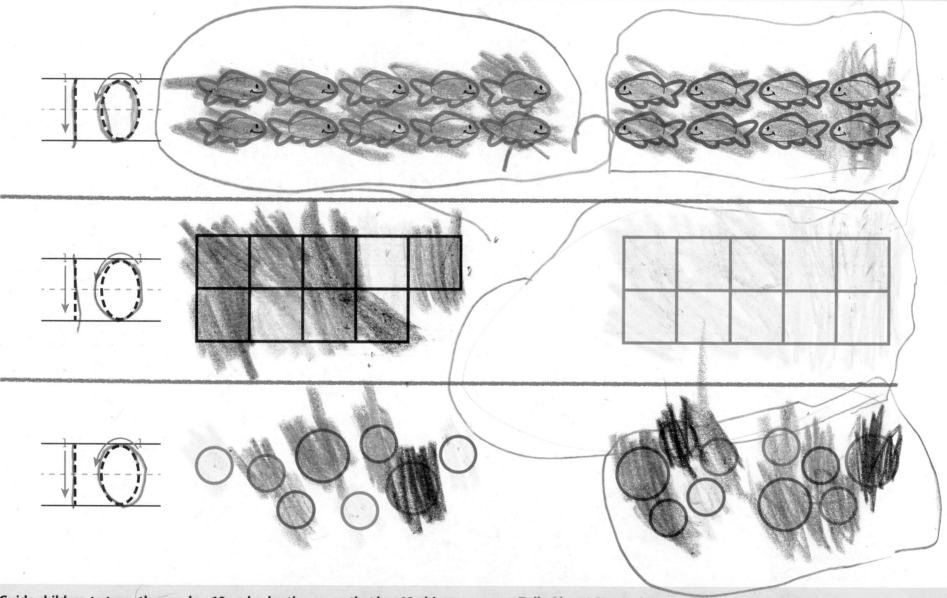

Guide children to trace the number 10 and color the group that has 10 objects.
Have children count the number of objects in both groups. Discuss different ways to count the objects. Then have them color the group that has 10.

<u>Talk About It</u> Work with a partner. Which problem made you think the most? Why?

Count 10

Name _____

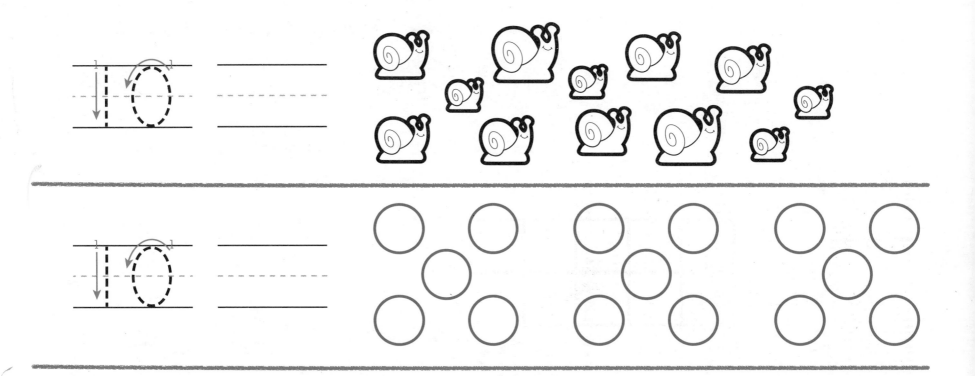

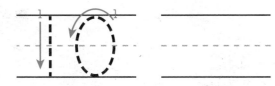

Guide children to trace and write the number 10 and then color 10 objects. Note that they may choose to color any 10 of the objects in the group. In the last problem, have children trace and write 10 and then draw 10 shapes or objects.

<u>Talk About It</u> Work with a partner. How did your partner draw 10? How can you check that you both drew 10 objects correctly?

©Curriculum Associates, LLC   Copying is not permitted.

Guided Practice • Lesson 11   65

Count 10

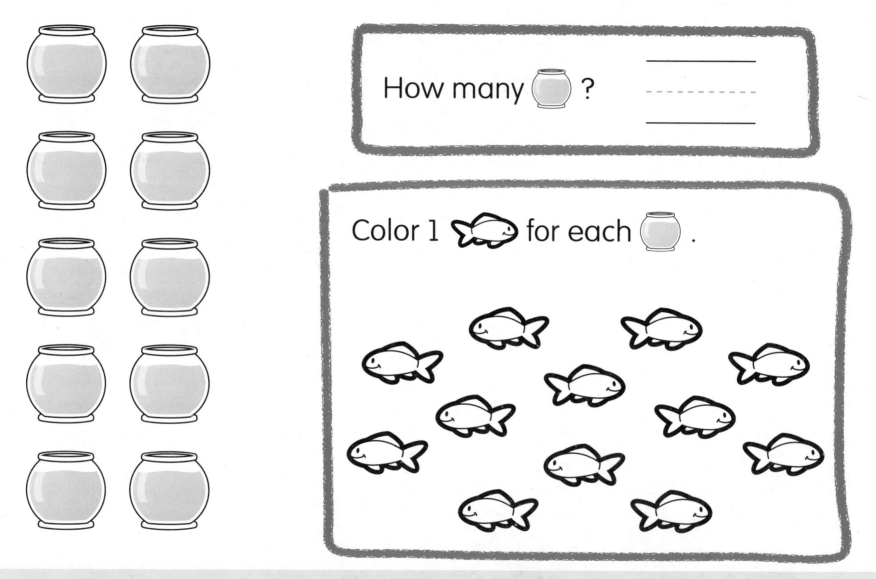

How many 🏺 ? _____

Color 1 🐟 for each 🏺.

Have children count and write the number of fishbowls and then color 1 fish for each bowl. Allow children to find their own strategies to figure out how many fish and which ones to color.

<u>Talk About It</u> Work with a partner. Did you color the same fish as your partner? How many fish do not have a bowl?

Compare Within 10

Children compare groups of 6 and 7 crayons and discuss how to identify the group that has more. Invite two children to the front of the class and give one child 6 crayons and the other 7 crayons. Ask: *Which child has more crayons?*

How do you know? Then have children use counters to model the problem and discuss how they can compare the number of counters without counting.

Children compare groups of counters to see which has more. Pair children and give each child a group of 5, 6, or 7 counters. Then ask children to compare the counters to find out which child has more or if they have the same number of counters. Ask pairs to explain how they determined who has more. Then display 5 crayons in one hand and 7 crayons in the other. Ask: *Which hand has more crayons? How do you know?*

Compare Within 10

Name _____

Encourage children to discuss the quantities of items and then compare quantities.
Guide children to make comparison statements using *more, less,* or *fewer.* Have children draw lines matching each puppy to a collar.

<u>Talk About It</u> What do you think most people buy at the pet store? Why?

Compare Within 10

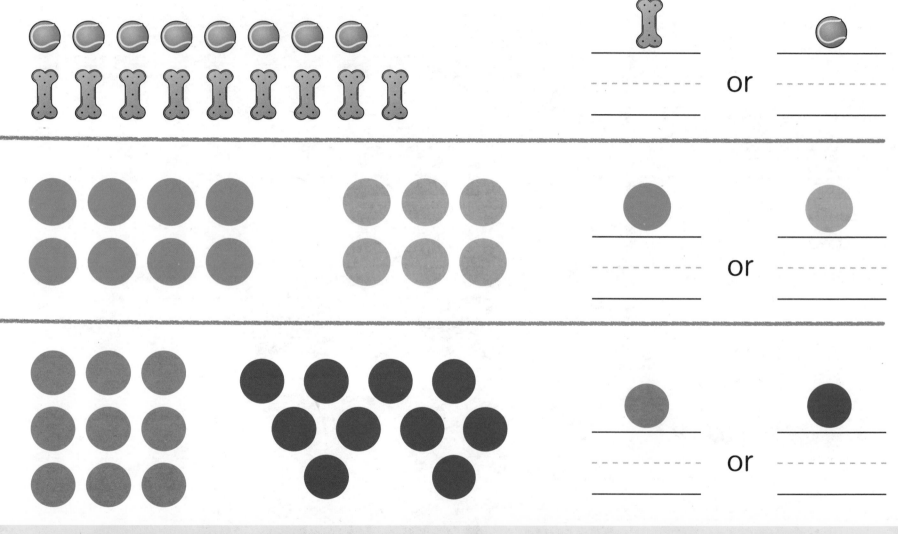

Guide children to compare the quantities shown in the pictures. Have children write how many in each group, then circle the number that is more. For each problem, discuss different ways to decide which group has more.

<u>Talk About It</u> Work with a partner. Look at the green and pink dots. Is there one pink dot for every green dot? How can you be sure?

Compare Within 10

Name _____

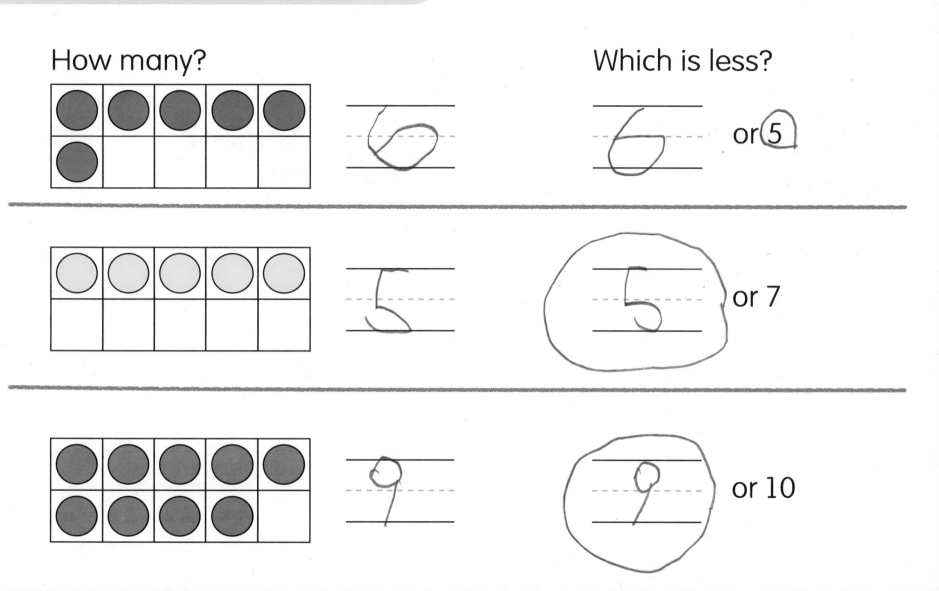

How many?

Which is less?

6   6   or ⑤

5   ⑤   or 7

9   ⑨   or 10

Guide children to compare the number of counters in a 10-frame with a given number and tell which is less. Have them count and write the number of counters in the 10-frame. Compare that number to the number shown in black. Circle the number that is less.

<u>Talk About It</u> Look at all the counters. Which group of counters shows the number closest to 10? How do you know?

Compare Within 10

Draw more.

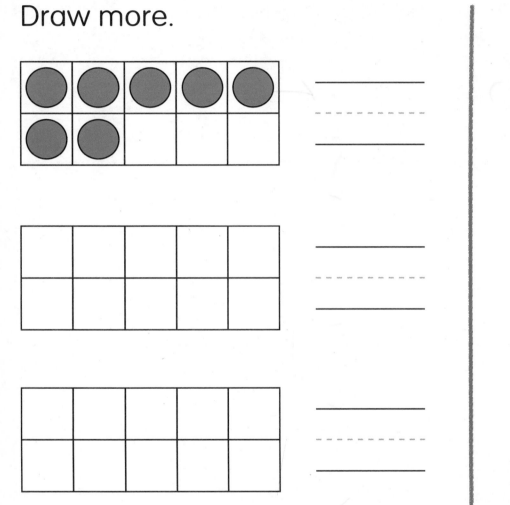

Draw less.

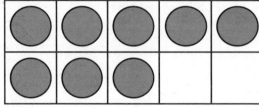

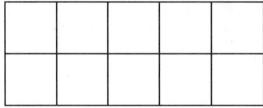

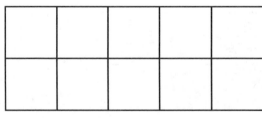

Have children draw more or less than a given number of counters. Have children count the given number of counters. For the blue counters, draw counters and write numbers to show more. For the red counters, draw counters and write numbers to show less.

Talk About It Check your work. How can you be sure you drew more? How can you be sure you drew less?

Make 10

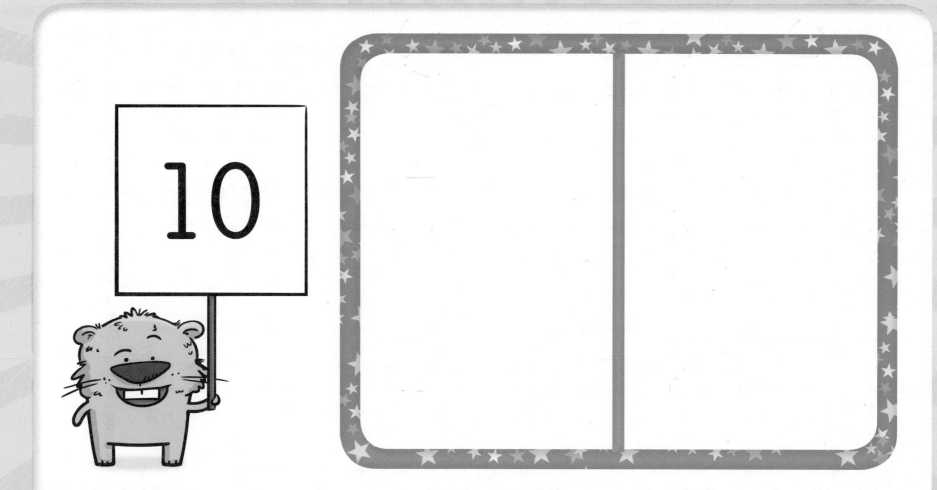

Children explore different ways to make 10 using boys and girls, then with two different colors of counters. Pose the problem: *How many ways can you make a group of 10 children with some number of boys and some number of girls?* Invite different groups of 10 boys and girls to the front of the room to model combinations of 10. Have children verbalize how each combination is made, then model the combination with connecting cubes.

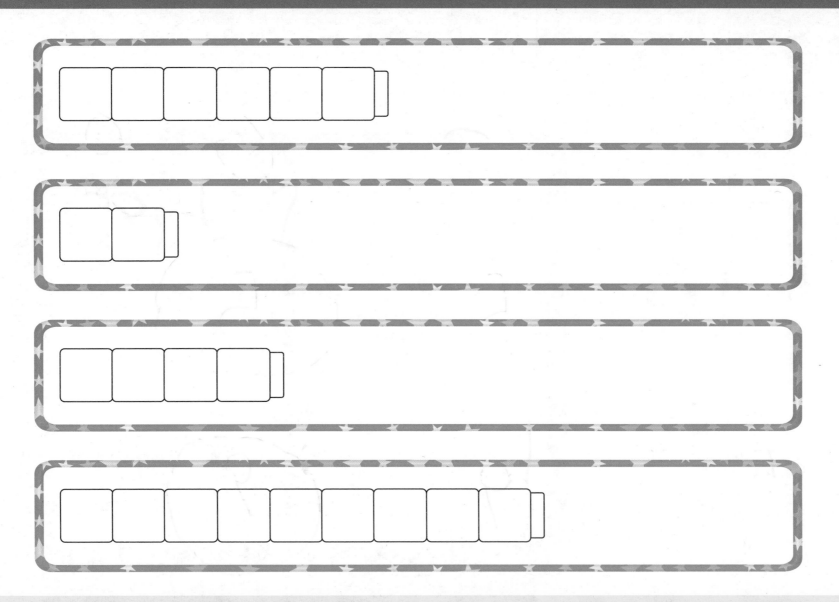

Children make combinations of 10 starting from a given number.
Display a train of 6 cubes. Ask: *How many more cubes do I need to have 10?*

Have children model the problem using connecting cubes. Repeat, starting with 2, 4, and 9 cubes.

Encourage children to describe the number of each type of ball as the total of two lesser numbers. Guide children to identify the number pairs shown for each group of 10 balls. Have children draw more red balls to make 10.

Talk About It How are the number of baseball bats and the number of baseballs the same? How are they different?

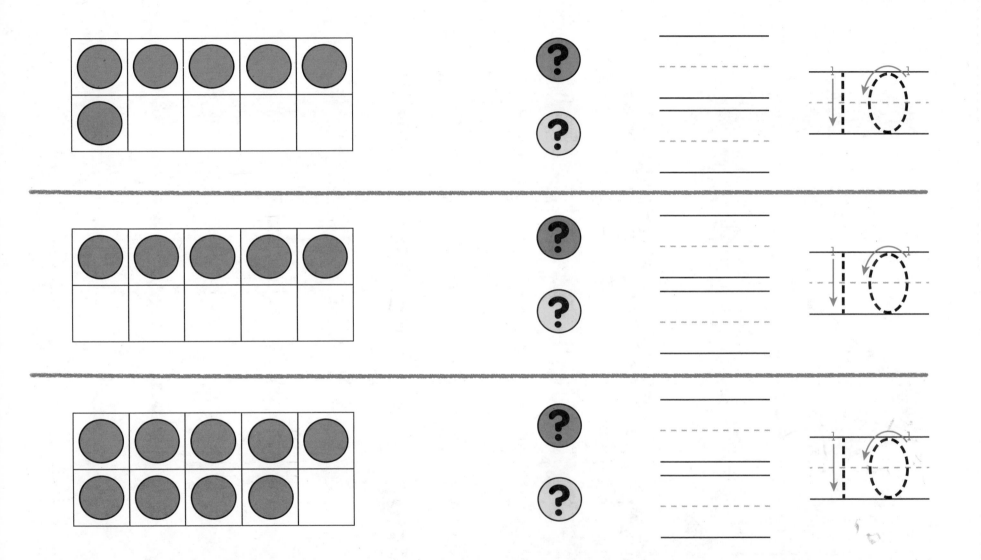

Guide children to draw yellow counters to finish each picture so that it shows 10. Then count and write how many counters there are of each color and trace the number 10.

<u>Talk About It</u> If you have 6 yellow counters, how many red counters would there be? How do you know?

©Curriculum Associates, LLC   Copying is not permitted.

Name _____

Understand Addition

5

_____ and _____

_____ and _____

_____ and _____

_____ and _____

Children explore the meaning of addition by making connections between concrete and verbal representations. Have 3 children come to the front of the room. Ask: *How many children are there? What can I do to make 5?*

Write "3 and 2" on the board and have children record. Repeat, starting with 2, 1, and 4 children, having children record the number pair each time. Introduce *add* as a word for joining numbers.

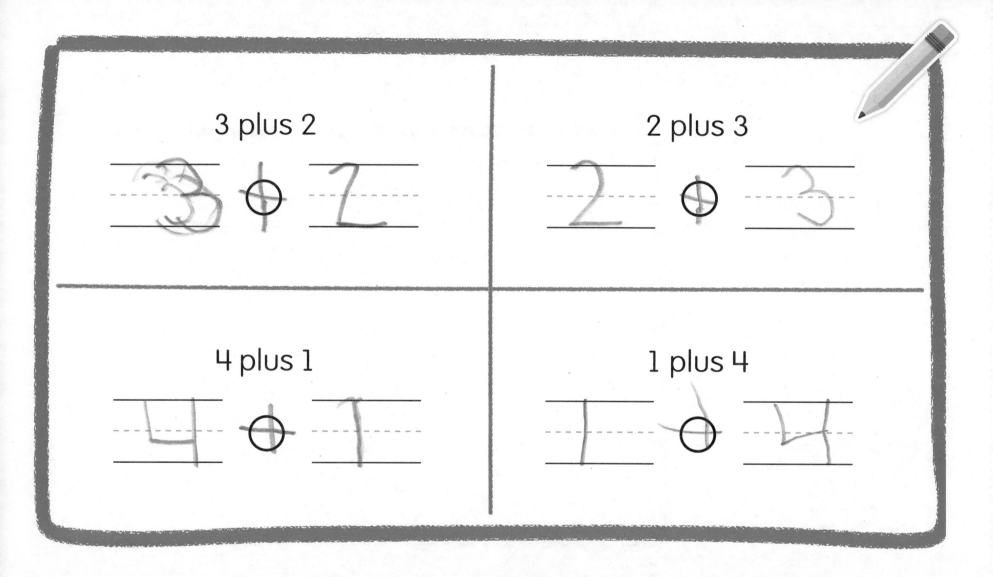

3 plus 2

2 plus 3

4 plus 1

1 plus 4

Children are introduced to the plus sign to represent addition. Tell children that *plus* is another word that can be used instead of *and*. Read each number pair aloud using the word *and* then again replacing the word *and* with *plus*. Introduce the plus sign as the symbol that stands for *plus*. Guide children to write each number pair using the plus sign. Then have children model each expression using fingers.

Name Yasin Moh

What can you add?

2 + 1

Ask children to draw a picture of things they might add together to show 2 + 1. For example, they might draw 2 crayons and 1 more crayon. Have children share and discuss their drawings, using the terms *plus* and *add*.

Talk About It Tell a story about why you might want to add the objects in your drawing.

Explore Together
Understand Addition

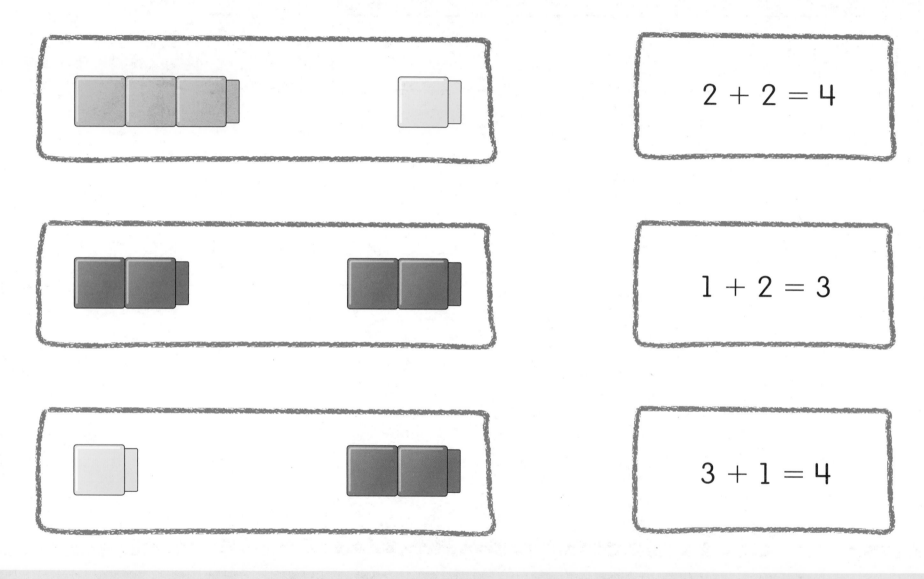

2 + 2 = 4

1 + 2 = 3

3 + 1 = 4

Guide children to match addition sentences to pictures. Have children describe how many cubes are being added in each picture. Read each number sentence aloud together and discuss the meaning of each. Then have children draw lines to match.

Talk About It How can you find the total number of cubes in each picture?

Think and Check
Understand Addition

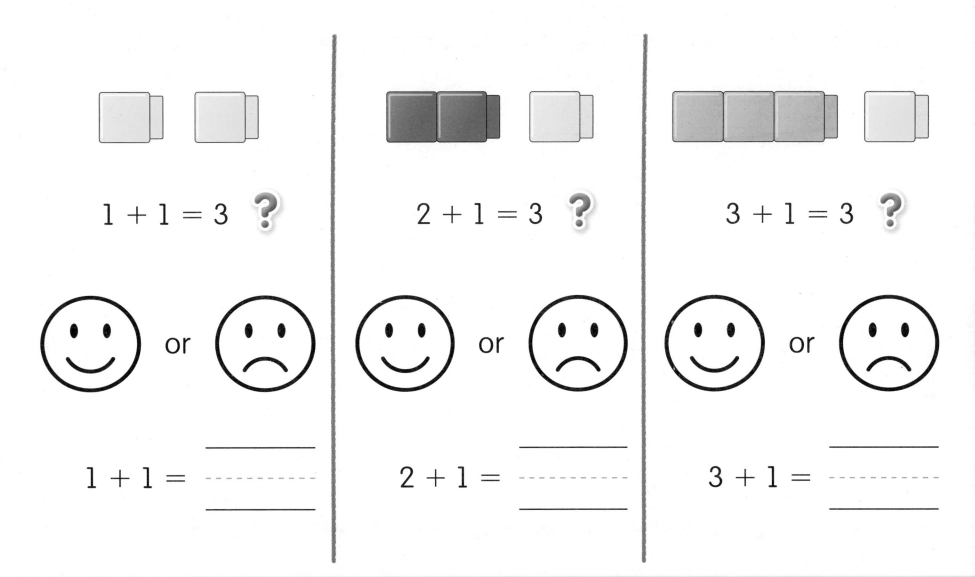

1 + 1 = 3 **?**

2 + 1 = 3 **?**

3 + 1 = 3 **?**

or

or

or

1 + 1 = _____

2 + 1 = _____

3 + 1 = _____

Guide children to check whether the number sentence matches the cubes. First discuss the groups of cubes, then the number sentence below them. Color the happy face if they match or the sad face if they don't. Guide children to complete the number sentence correctly.

<u>Talk About It</u> Explain how you figured out how to fix each mistake you found.

Understand Addition

Draw _____ + _____ = 5.

Have children draw a picture showing two groups of objects that can be added to get a total of 5. There are many possible ways children can draw their pictures. Have children hold up their pictures to share. Discuss the different ways children grouped the objects to make 5.

<u>Talk About It</u>   What other ways can you think of to show two groups that total 5?

Add Within 5

_____ + _____ = _____

Children use a 5-frame and counters to represent and solve an addition word problem and read a corresponding number sentence. Invite 1 girl and 2 boys to act out boarding a bus. Say: *1 girl and 2 boys get on the bus.*

How many children are on the bus? Have children use counters and the 5-frame to model the problem. Write the corresponding number sentence on the board. Have children record the sentence. Read the sentence together.

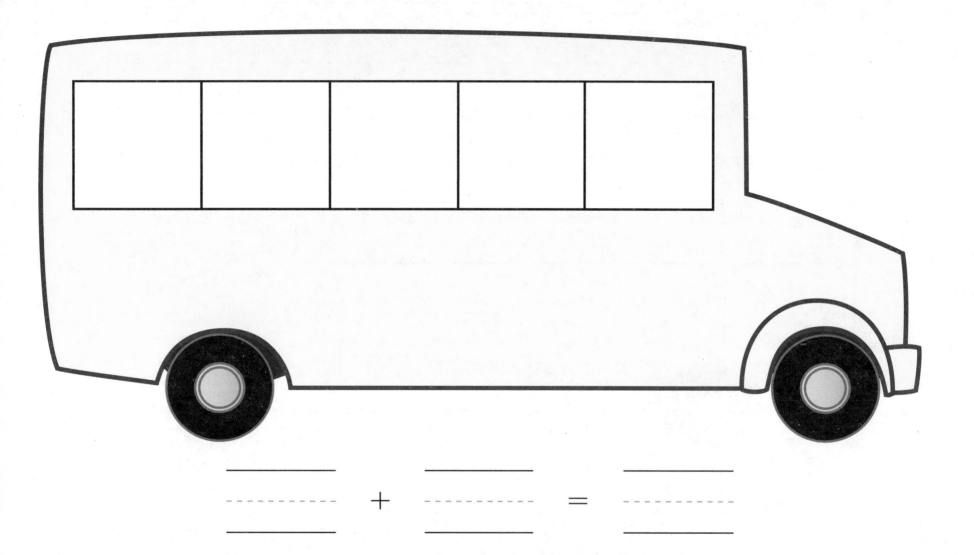

$$\overline{} + \overline{} = \overline{}$$

Children use a 5-frame and counters to act out another addition problem and read a corresponding number sentence. Say: *There are 3 children on the bus. 1 girl gets on the bus. How many children are on the bus now?*

Have children use counters and the 5-frame to model the problem. Have children help you complete the number sentence on the board. Then children record the number sentence. Read the sentence aloud together.

Encourage children to describe addition problems for each group of animals. Provide an example, such as 3 little pigs and 1 big pig is 4 pigs. Have children circle the two groups of animals that show 3 plus 1.

<u>Talk About It</u>   How is the group of sheep like the group of pigs?

2 + 1 = _____

3 + 1 = _____

2 + 2 = _____

2 + 3 = _____

Guide children to compare each number sentence to the pictured addition problem, then count and write the total. Have them read the completed number sentence aloud. Help children connect the written total with the number of animals shown.

<u>Talk About It</u> Which is more, 2 + 1 or 3 + 1? How can you tell?

Practice Together
Add Within 5

Name _____

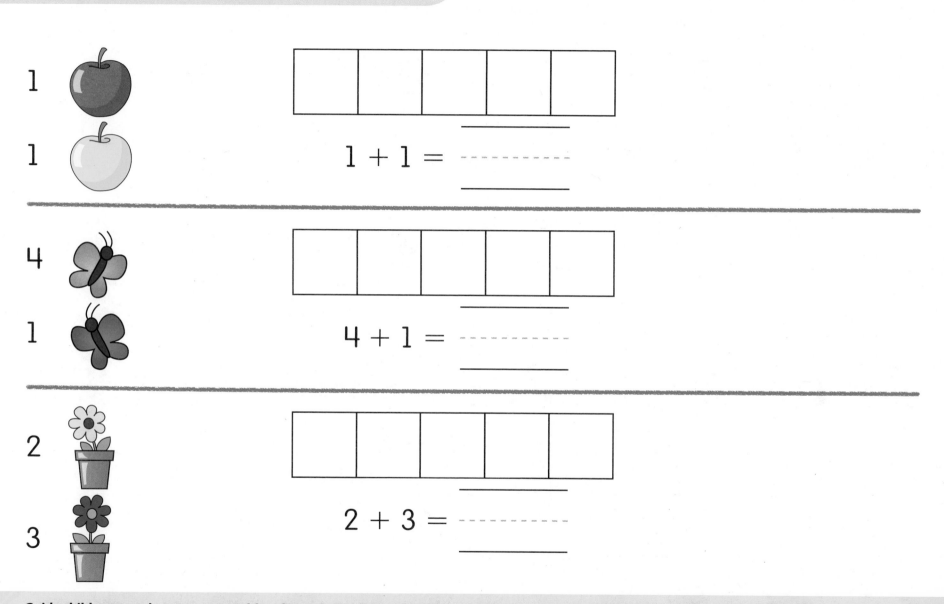

1

1

$1 + 1 =$ -------

4

1

$4 + 1 =$ -------

2

3

$2 + 3 =$ -------

Guide children to make up a story problem for each situation, color the 5-frame to model the story, then count and write the total. Read the completed number sentence aloud and connect the written total with the story problem.

Talk About It Which two problems have the same total?

Add Within 5

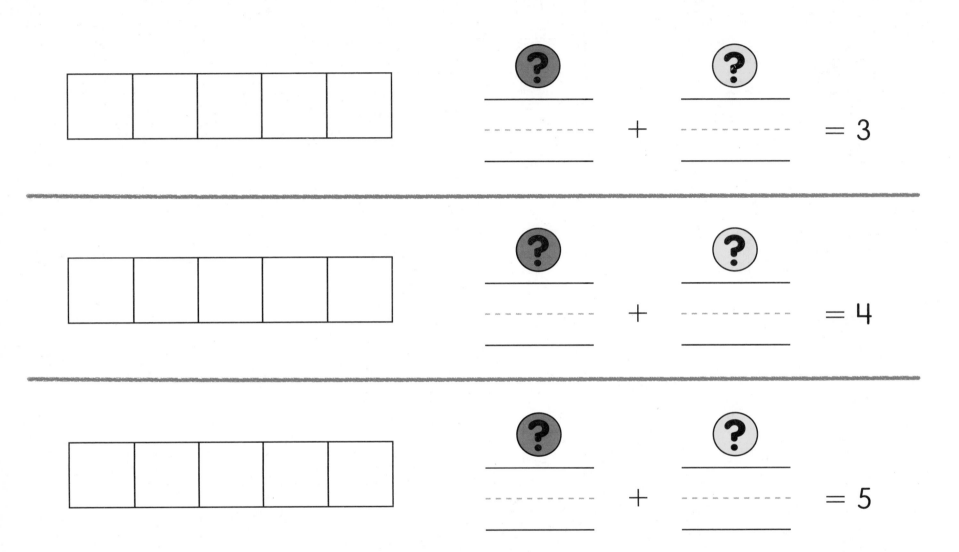

Have children choose two numbers to make each total. Have them color the 5-frame with red and yellow counters to show those numbers, then write the numbers to complete the number sentence. Explain that there are multiple correct answers.

<u>Talk About It</u>　Think of an addition story you could tell using the numbers in each problem.

Understand Subtraction

Children explore the meaning of subtraction by making connections between concrete and verbal representations. Invite 3 children to the front of the room. Have children act out 3 take away 2. Have children use counters to model the problem on the workmat. Write "3 take away 2" on the board. Repeat with other number pairs with totals within 5. Introduce *subtract* as a term for breaking apart numbers.

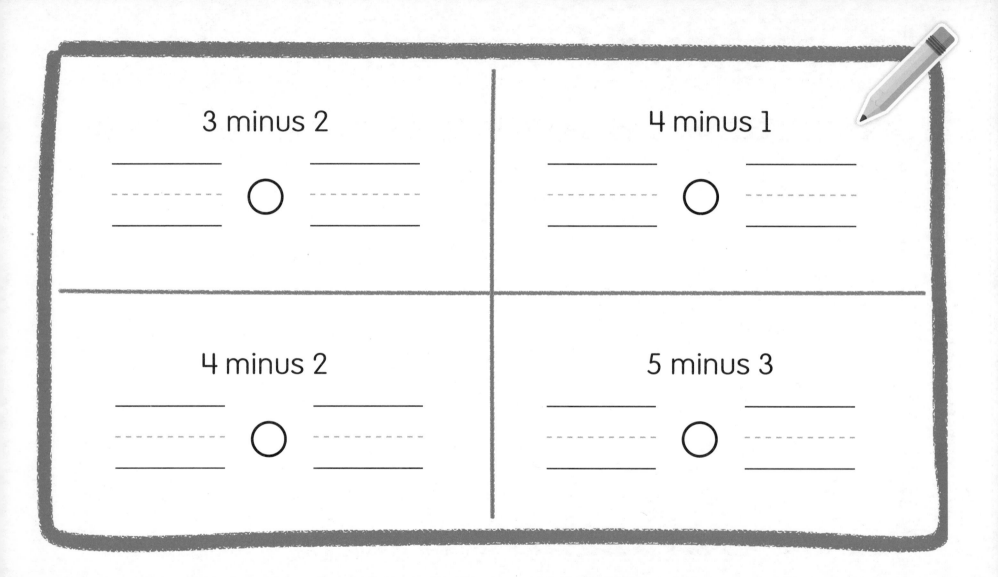

3 minus 2

4 minus 1

4 minus 2

5 minus 3

Children are introduced to the minus sign to represent subtraction.
Tell children that *minus* is a word that can be used instead of *take away*.
Read each take-away statement aloud, then read again, this time replacing

take away with *minus*. Introduce the minus sign as the symbol that stands
for *minus*. Guide children to complete each expression using the minus sign.
Have children model each expression using fingers.

Name _____

Why do you subtract?

3 − 1

Ask children to draw a picture that could show 3 take away 1. For example, they might draw 3 books with 1 book crossed out. Have children share and discuss their drawings, using the terms *take away*, *minus*, and *subtract*.

Talk About It   Why did you take away one of the objects in your drawing?

Match.

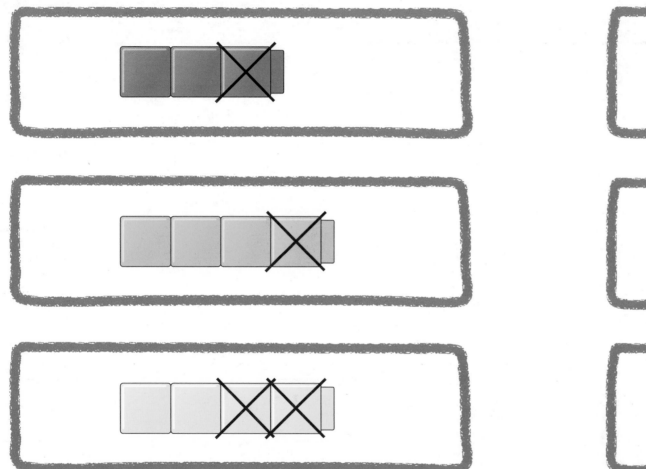

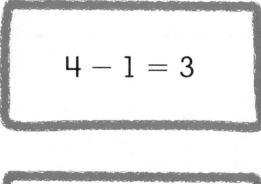

$$4 - 1 = 3$$

$$4 - 2 = 2$$

$$3 - 1 = 2$$

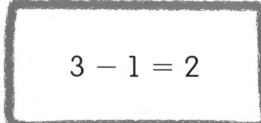

Guide children to match each picture to a number sentence. Discuss the number of cubes in each picture, and how many are taken away. Read and discuss the meaning of each number sentence. Then have children draw lines to match.

Talk About It How can you check your answers to make sure the picture matches the number sentence you chose?

Think and Check
Understand Subtraction

Name _____

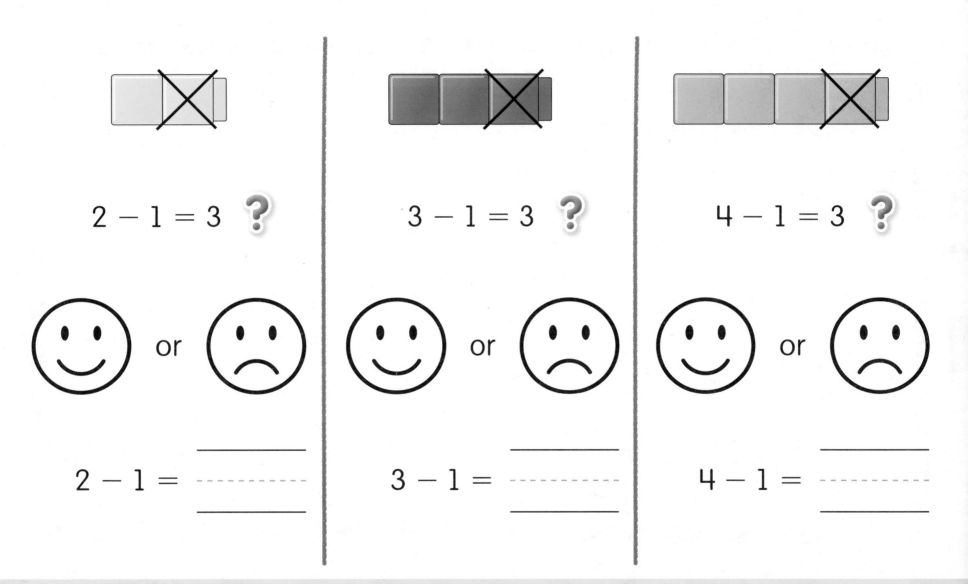

$2 - 1 = 3$?

☺ or ☹

$2 - 1 =$ _____

$3 - 1 = 3$?

☺ or ☹

$3 - 1 =$ _____

$4 - 1 = 3$?

☺ or ☹

$4 - 1 =$ _____

Guide children to decide if each number sentence is correct or not. Discuss whether each picture matches the number sentence shown. Have children color the happy face if correct, the sad face if not. Then guide children to complete the number sentence correctly.

<u>**Talk About It**</u> Explain how you figured out how to fix each mistake you found.

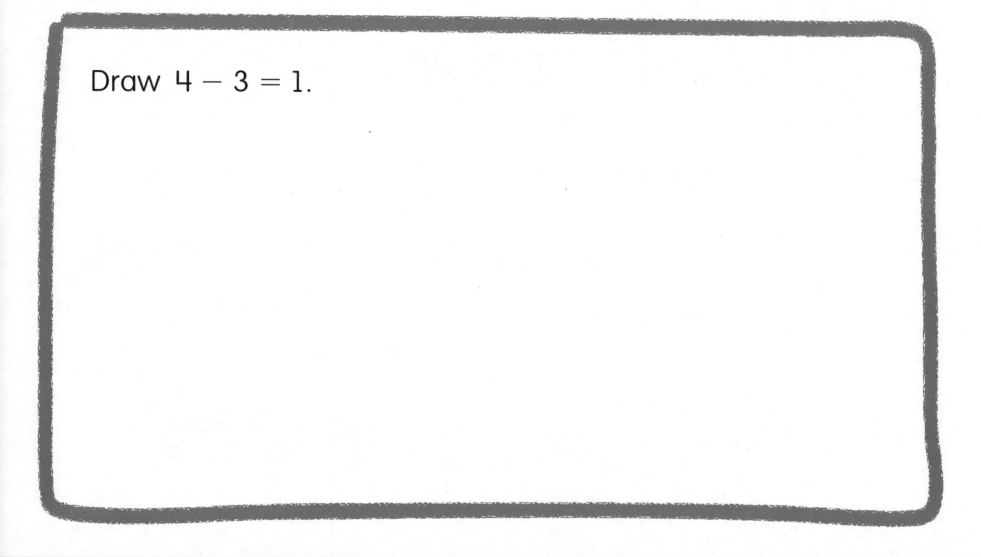

Draw 4 − 3 = 1.

Have children draw a picture to show that 4 minus 3 is 1. Afterward, have children hold up their pictures to share. Encourage children to find what is the same about all the drawings.

Talk About It What is a story you could tell about your picture?

Name _____

Subtract Within 5

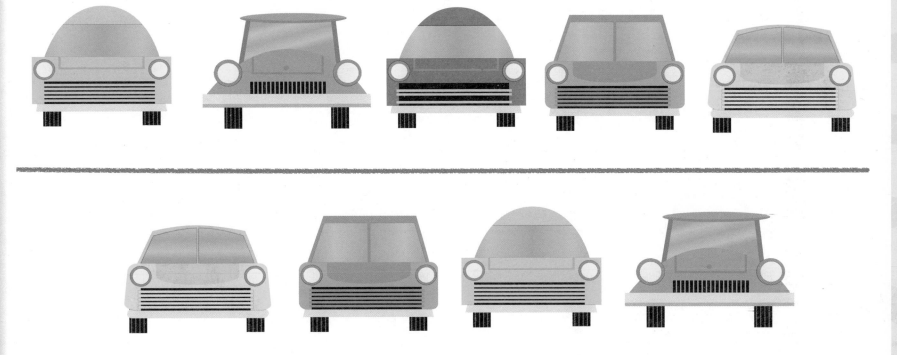

Have children act out subtraction word problems and record the corresponding number sentences. Pose the problem: *In a parking lot, there are 5 cars parked in a row. 1 car leaves. How many cars are still in the row?*

Act out the subtraction. Model the subtraction. Solve another problem: *There are 4 cars in a row. 2 cars leave the row. How many cars are left in the row?*

Children use counters and their fingers to model other subtraction problems. Say: *Adam has 4 crayons. He gives 1 to his sister. How many crayons does Adam have left?* Ask children to use counters to show the subtraction.

Repeat, saying: *Adam has 5 crayons. He gives 2 to his sister. How many crayons does Adam have left now?* Ask children to use their fingers to model and solve the problem.

Subtract Within 5

Name _____

Encourage children to describe subtraction problems for each group of objects.
Provide the example: *There were 5 candles but 4 are gone. Now there's only 1 candle left.*
Have children circle the groups of objects that show 5 minus 2.

<u>Talk About It</u> If somebody eats another slice of cake, how many will be left?

Subtract Within 5

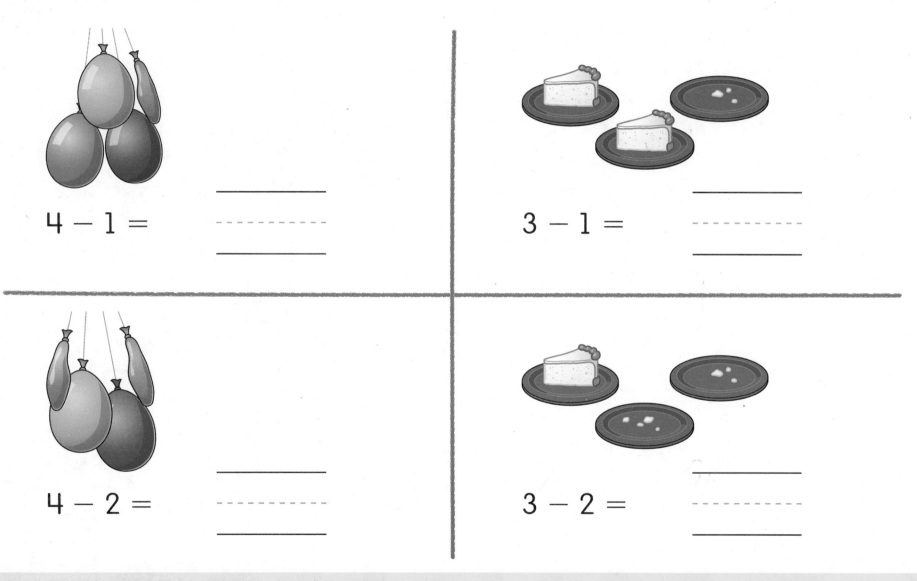

4 − 1 = _____

3 − 1 = _____

4 − 2 = _____

3 − 2 = _____

Guide children to compare each number sentence to the subtraction picture, then count and write the number left. Have them read the completed number sentence aloud. Help children connect the written numbers with the number of objects shown.

<u>**Talk About It**</u> Can you tell a subtraction story about the cake plates?

©Curriculum Associates, LLC   Copying is not permitted.

$$2 - 1 = \underline{}$$

$$4 - 2 = \underline{}$$

$$5 - 3 = \underline{}$$

Guide children to make up a story problem for each situation. Then count and write the number left. Have children read the completed number sentence aloud and connect the written numbers with the story problem.

<u>Talk About It</u> Work with a partner. Tell two different stories about the balloon problem.

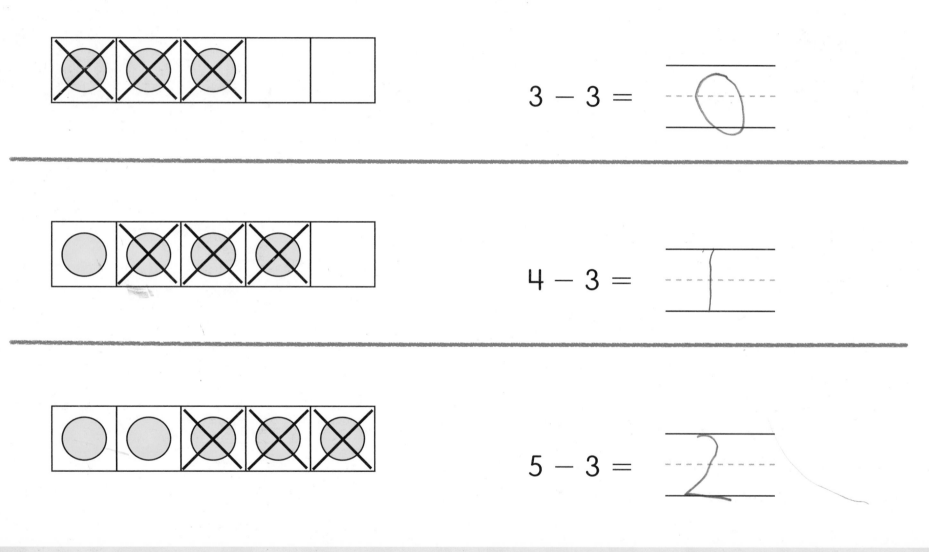

$3 - 3 = \underline{}$ 0

$4 - 3 = \underline{}$ 1

$5 - 3 = \underline{}$ 2

Have children complete each number sentence. Afterward, ask children to tell how they found the answers. Some may have used the pictures, and some may have used other strategies.

<u>Talk About It</u> What pattern do you see when you look at your answers? What pattern do you see when you look at the pictures?

Add Within 10

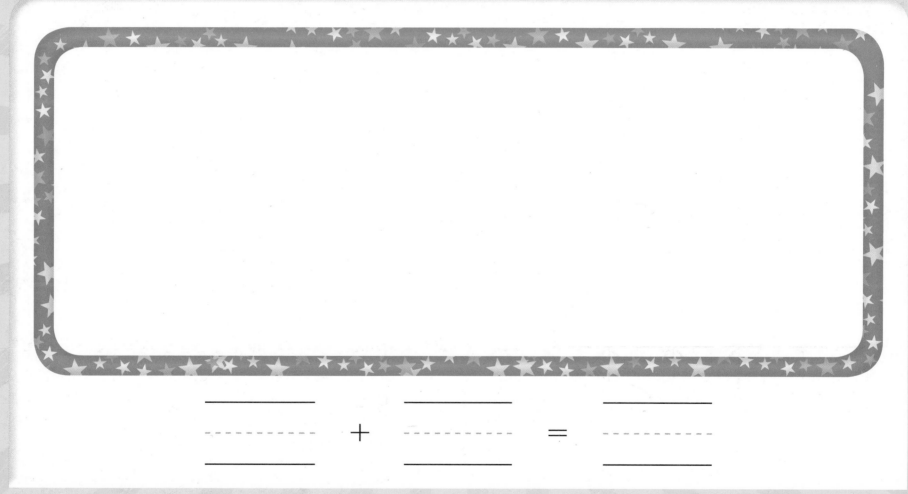

_____   +   _____   =   _____

Children act out and solve an addition problem and record a corresponding number sentence. Say: *4 children are siting at a table. 2 more children join them. How many children are sitting at the table now?*

Have children act out the problem, then model the problem with counters. Discuss how to show this as a number sentence. Write 4 + 2 = 6 on the board and have children record it.

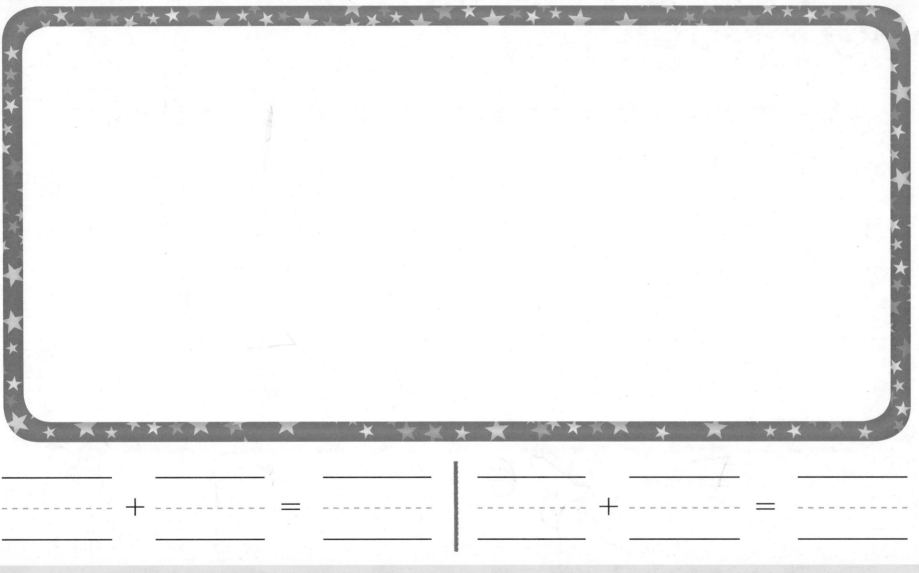

_____ + _____ = _____ | _____ + _____ = _____

Children act out and solve addition situations. Say: _There are 3 children at a table. 4 more children join them. How many children are at the table?_ Have children act out the problem and then use counters to model it. Write the corresponding number sentence and relate it to both the children and the counters. Have children record the sentence. Repeat, saying: _3 children are sitting at the table. 2 children are standing at the table. How many children are at the table in all?_

PET STORE

Encourage children to tell addition story problems for various groups of objects. Ask children to discuss the addition facts shown by each group of objects, in more than one way if possible. Have children circle the group that shows 4 + 3 = 7.

Talk About It How many dogs will there be if one more comes into the store? How do you know?

Add Within 10

$7 + 1 =$ _____

$6 + 3 =$ _____

$8 + 2 =$ _____

$7 + 3 =$ _____

Guide children to compare each picture to the addition sentence, then count and write the total. Have them read the completed number sentence aloud. Help children connect the written total with the total number of objects shown.

<u>Talk About It</u>   How did you find the total of each group? How could you check your answer?

Add Within 10

Name _____

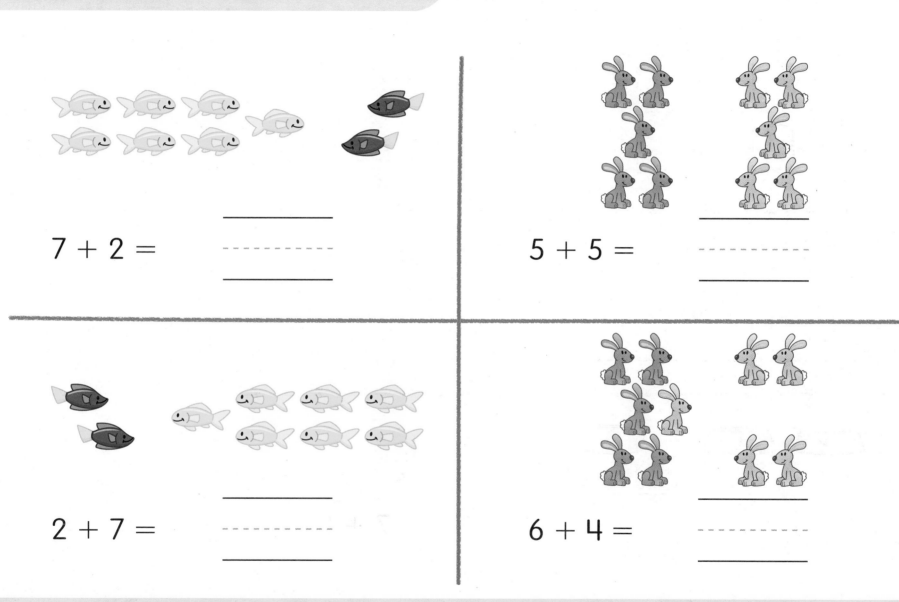

7 + 2 = _____

5 + 5 = _____

2 + 7 = _____

6 + 4 = _____

Guide children to compare each picture to the addition sentence, then count and write the total. Have them read the completed number sentence aloud. Help children connect the written total with the total number of animals shown.

<u>Talk About It</u> Compare the two problems about rabbits. What is the same and what is different?

Add Within 10

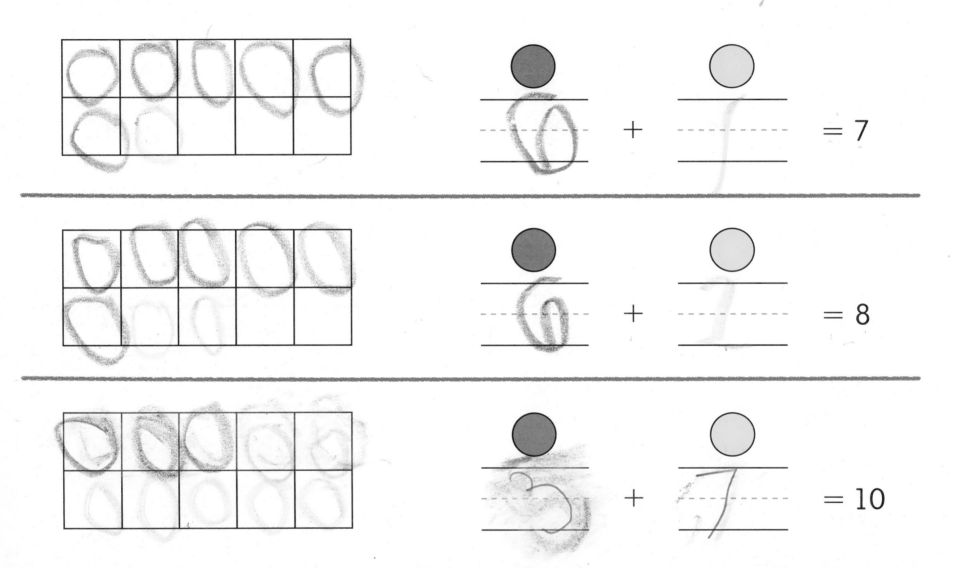

6 + 1 = 7

6 + 2 = 8

3 + 7 = 10

Have children find two numbers to make a given total. Have children color the 10-frame with red and yellow to show their numbers. Then have them write their numbers to complete the number sentence. Explain that multiple correct answers are possible.

<u>Talk About It</u> Work with a partner. Are your number sentences the same? Are your number sentences correct?

Subtract Within 10

$$7 - 1 = \underline{}$$

$$7 - 2 = \underline{}$$

Have children act out subtraction word problems and record the corresponding number sentences. Say: *There are 7 birds sitting on a branch. 1 bird flies away. How many birds are still on the branch?* Have children cover 1 bird using an index card. Guide children to complete a subtraction sentence to represent the story problem. Repeat with the problem: *There are 7 birds on a branch. 2 birds fly away. How many birds are still on the branch?*

Subtract Within 10

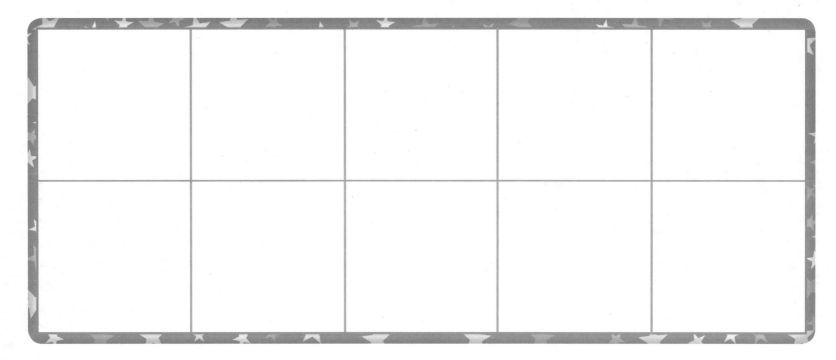

$8 - 1 = $ _____

$8 - 2 = $ _____

Children solve more subtraction word problems using counters and record corresponding number sentences. Say: *Katie has 8 pennies. She gives 1 to her brother. How many pennies does Katie have left for herself?* Have children show the problem with counters on the 10-frame, then complete the corresponding subtraction sentence. Repeat with the situation: *Will has 8 pennies. He gives 2 to his sister. How many pennies does Will have left for himself?*

Explore Together
Subtract Within 10

Name Yasin/Lieanne

Encourage children to describe take-away situations they see in the picture. For each group of items, have children circle the ones that are left after the others are taken away.

<u>Talk About It</u>   How do the flowers show a take-away story?

Subtract Within 10

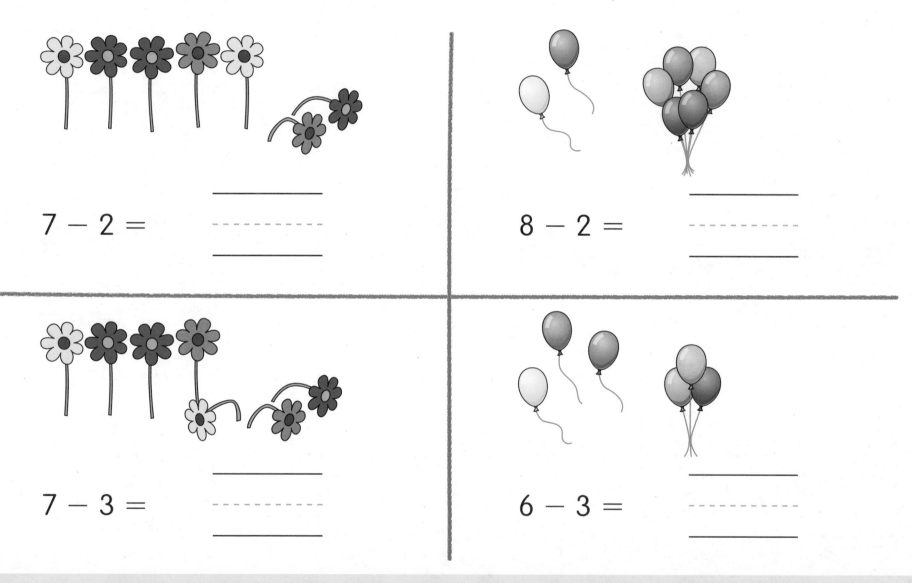

7 − 2 = _____

8 − 2 = _____

7 − 3 = _____

6 − 3 = _____

Guide children to compare the picture to the number sentence to answer the subtraction problem. Guide children to cross out the objects being taken away with an X. Then have children complete the number sentence. Read each number sentence aloud together.

Talk About It   How did you know how many were left?

Subtract Within 10

Name _____

9 − 4 = _____

10 − 4 = _____

9 − 5 = _____

10 − 5 = _____

Guide children to compare the fingers showing the numbers to the number sentence to answer the subtraction problem. Have children put an X over fingers being taken away. Guide children to complete each number sentence. Read each number sentence aloud.

<u>Talk About It</u> How did you choose which fingers to "take away" in each problem?

Subtract Within 10

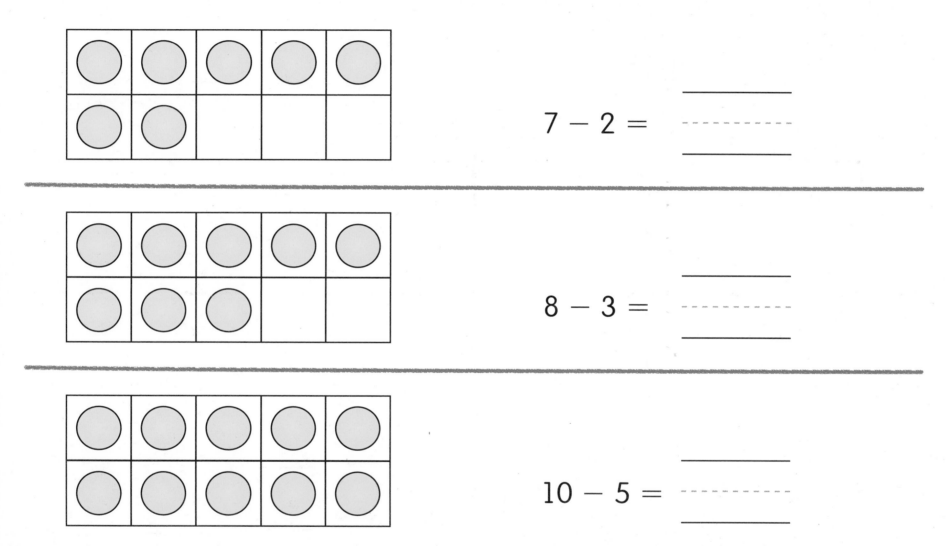

$7 - 2 =$ _____

$8 - 3 =$ _____

$10 - 5 =$ _____

Encourage children to use the pictures of the counters to help them solve each problem. Have children cross out the number of counters being taken away and complete the number sentence. Have children share how they used the model with the class.

Talk About It How are all the problems the same? How are they different?

Practice Facts to 5

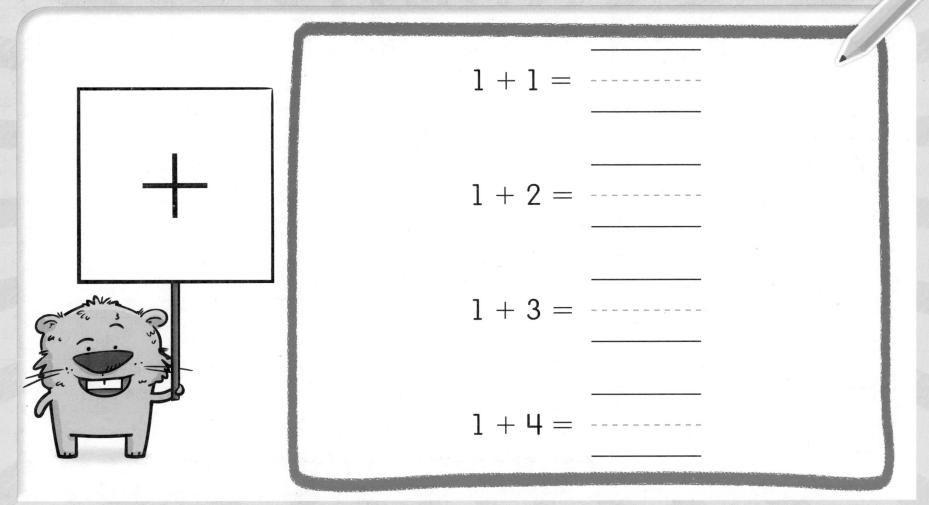

$$1 + 1 = \underline{\hspace{3cm}}$$

$$1 + 2 = \underline{\hspace{3cm}}$$

$$1 + 3 = \underline{\hspace{3cm}}$$

$$1 + 4 = \underline{\hspace{3cm}}$$

Children act out addition facts within 5, model with fingers, and write the total. Review the plus and equal signs. Write "1 + 1 = ___" on the board. Invite 1 child to the front of the class. Ask: *How many more children should stand to model this problem? What does the number of children standing show?* Complete the addition fact on the board. Repeat, adding 2, 3, and 4 to 1. Have children complete each number sentence and model each addition fact using fingers.

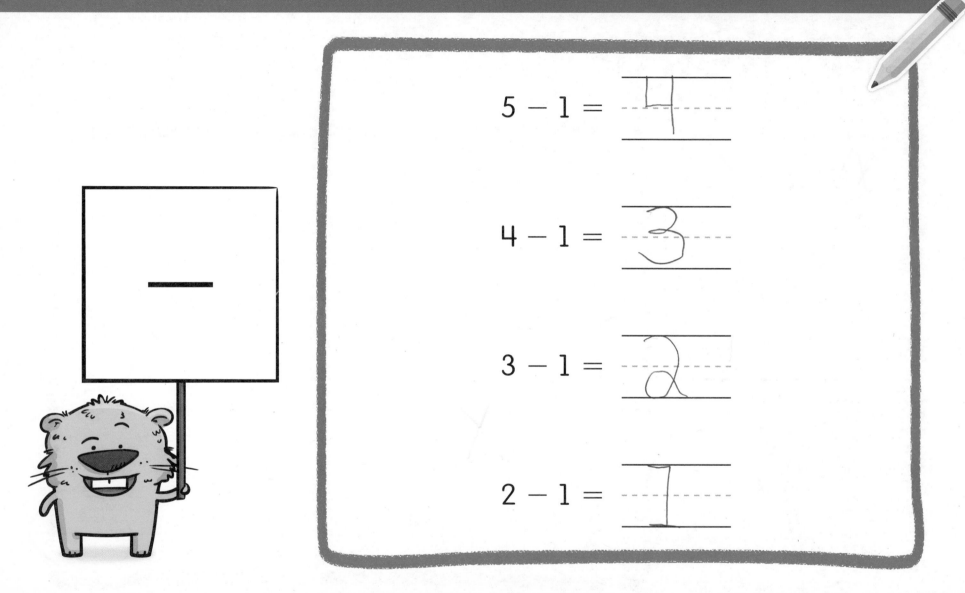

$$5 - 1 = \underline{4}$$

$$4 - 1 = \underline{3}$$

$$3 - 1 = \underline{2}$$

$$2 - 1 = \underline{1}$$

Children act out subtraction facts within 5, model with fingers, and write the difference. Invite 5 children to the front of the class. Write "5 – 1 = __" on the board. Ask: *What does this say? How many are left if we take 1 away from 5?*

Have children act out the problem. Complete the subtraction fact on the board. Repeat, subtracting 1 from 4, 3, and 2. Then children complete each number sentence and model each subtraction fact using fingers.

Name Yasin

Encourage children to tell story problems using addition and subtraction number sentences. Provide an example, such as: *The castle has 5 windows: 2 on top plus 3 below.* Have children put an X on objects they take away and circle the number left.

Talk About It What different number facts for 5 can you find?

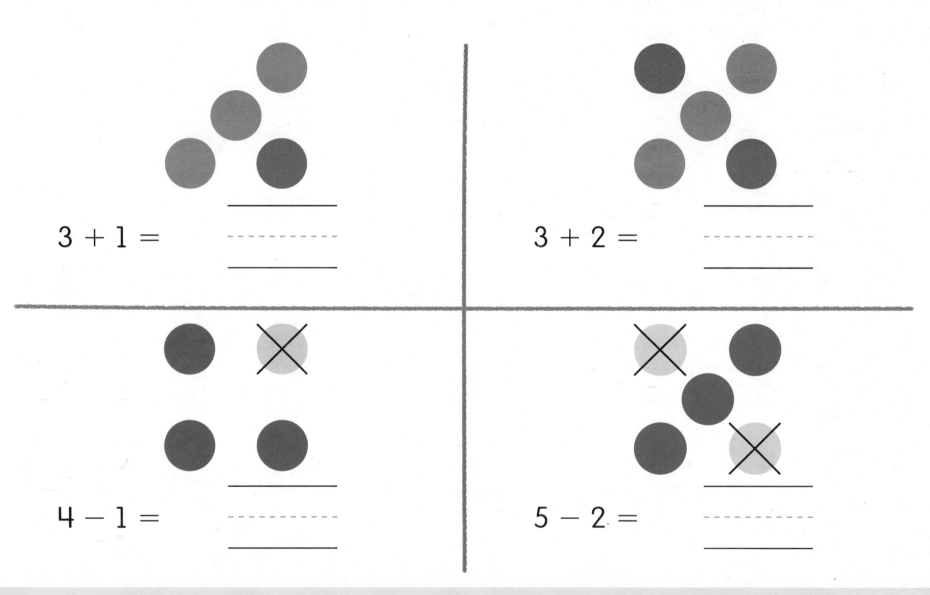

$3 + 1 =$ _____

$3 + 2 =$ _____

$4 - 1 =$ _____

$5 - 2 =$ _____

Guide children to use the picture to help them complete each number sentence. Read each number sentence. Guide children to look for patterns as they compare the number sentences. For example, 3 + 1 is 4, so if you start with 4 and take away 1, you get 3.

Talk About It How does the total for 3 + 1 compare to the total for 3 + 2? How do the addends compare?

Practice Facts to 5

Name _____

$\blacksquare = 1$ $\blacksquare = 2$ $\blacksquare = 3$ $\blacksquare = 4$ $\blacksquare = 5$

$1 + 1$	$2 + 2$	$4 - 2$	$2 + 3$	$5 - 2$
$1 + 2$	$2 + 1$	$3 - 1$	$3 + 2$	$5 - 3$
$1 + 3$	$3 + 1$	$4 - 1$	$5 - 4$	$3 - 2$
$1 + 4$	$4 + 1$	$5 - 1$	$4 - 3$	$2 - 1$

Guide children to color the facts based on the color of the answer shown at the top of the page. Discuss any number patterns in the rows and columns. Have children draw lines to connect the facts that have the same addends but in a different order.

<u>Talk About It</u> Why do you think that $4 + 1$ is the same color as $1 + 4$? What else is alike? Can you find some other facts that look like $4 + 1$ and $1 + 4$?

Practice Facts to 5

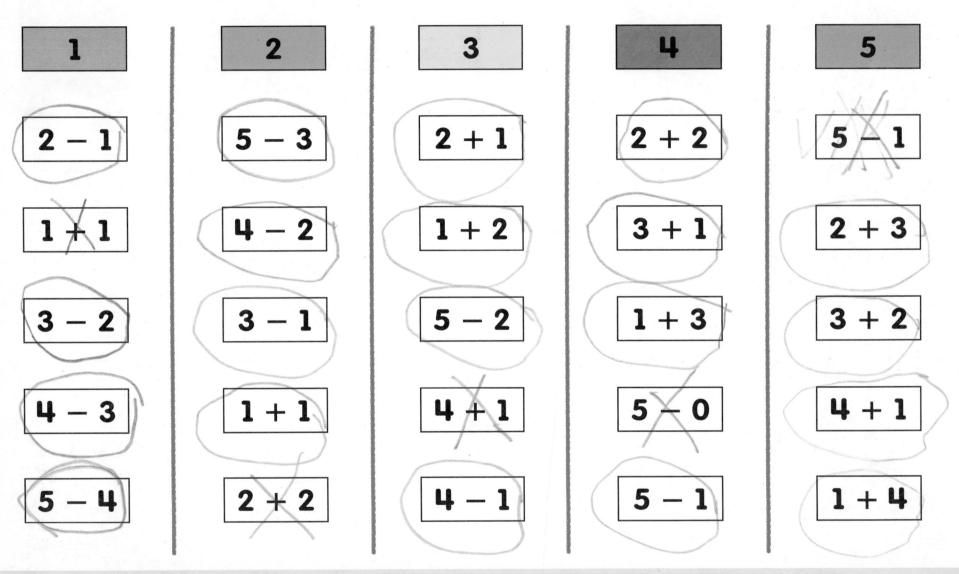

1	2	3	4	5
2 − 1	5 − 3	2 + 1	2 + 2	5 − 1
1 + 1	4 − 2	1 + 2	3 + 1	2 + 3
3 − 2	3 − 1	5 − 2	1 + 3	3 + 2
4 − 3	1 + 1	4 + 1	5 − 0	4 + 1
5 − 4	2 + 2	4 − 1	5 − 1	1 + 4

Have children look at the facts in each column and color all those that equal the number at the top. Have children draw an X on the facts that don't belong in each column. Discuss any patterns children notice for the facts that have the same answer.

<u>Talk About It</u> How did you decide which facts did not belong with the others?

120   Lesson 20 • Independent Practice

Name _____

Understand Teen Numbers

1	2	3	4	5	6	7	8	9	10
11	12	13	14	15	16	17	18	19	20

Children show teen numbers using fingers. Review rote counting to 20, having children point to each number as they count. Pose the question: *Can I show 11 with my fingers? Why not?* Guide children to the idea that two people can show 11 fingers. Have children work in pairs. Pose the question: *How many extra fingers do we need to make 12?* Say: *To make 12, we need all 10 fingers and 2 extra fingers.* Repeat for other teen numbers.

Children use 10-frames to show teen numbers and count to confirm there are 10 and some more ones. Provide pairs of children with between 11 and 19 counters. Have children fill the 10-frame with counters and place the left-over counters below the 10-frame. Have children predict the teen number they made. Ask: *How did you decide?* Then have children count to verify.

Understand Teen Numbers

Name _____

What are teen numbers?

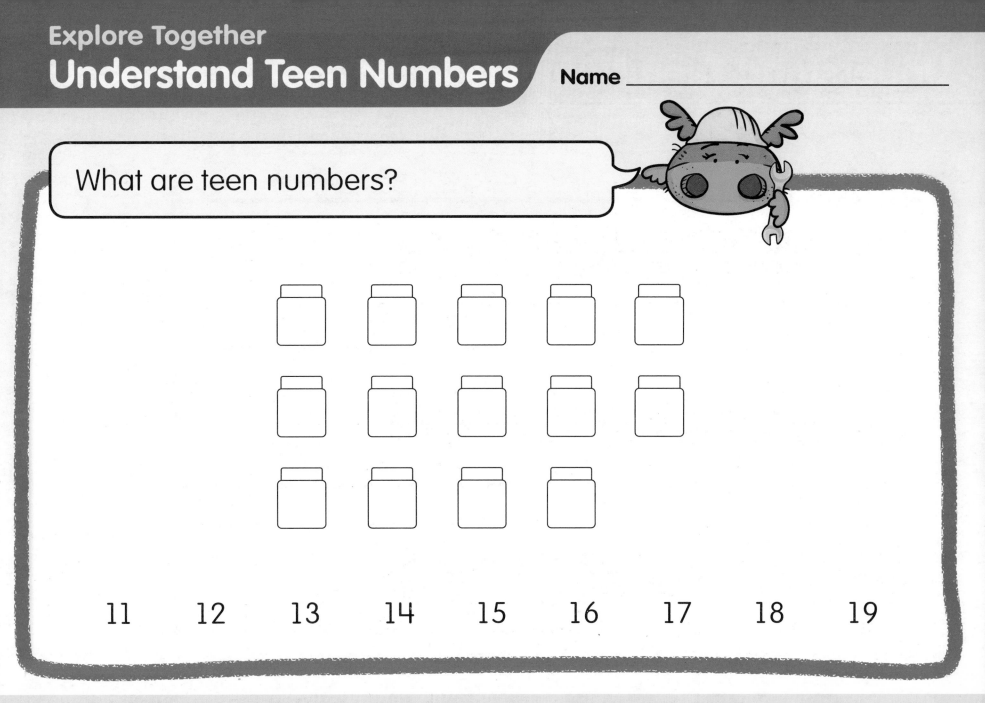

11   12   13   14   15   16   17   18   19

Encourage children to count the number of cubes together as a class. Then have children color a group of 10 cubes and circle their group of 10. Have them count the "extras." Have them color the extras a different color. Have children circle the number 14.

Talk About It When you look at a teen number, how can you tell how many "extras" there are?

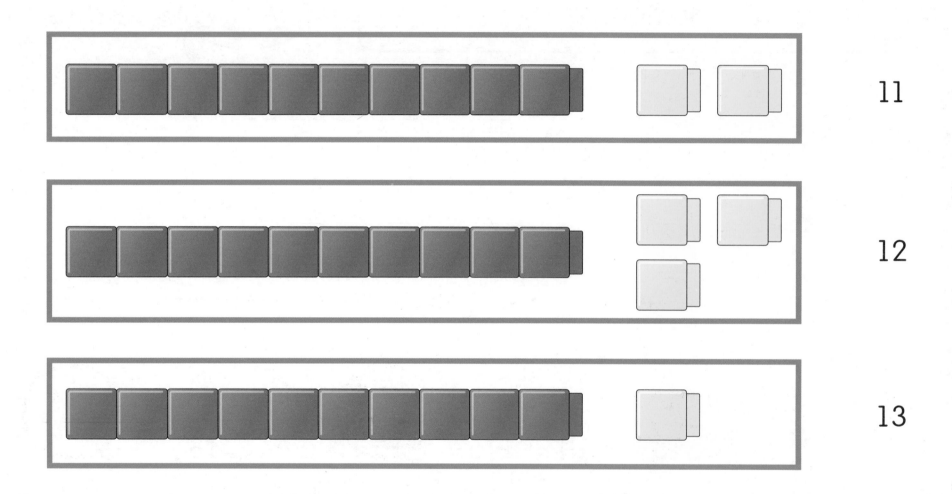

Guide children to match teen numbers to cubes that show the same number. Have children describe the cubes in each group as ten and some number of extras. Then have children draw lines to match the numbers to the pictures.

<u>Talk About It</u> How can you check your answers to make sure the picture matches the number you chose?

Think and Check
Understand Teen Numbers

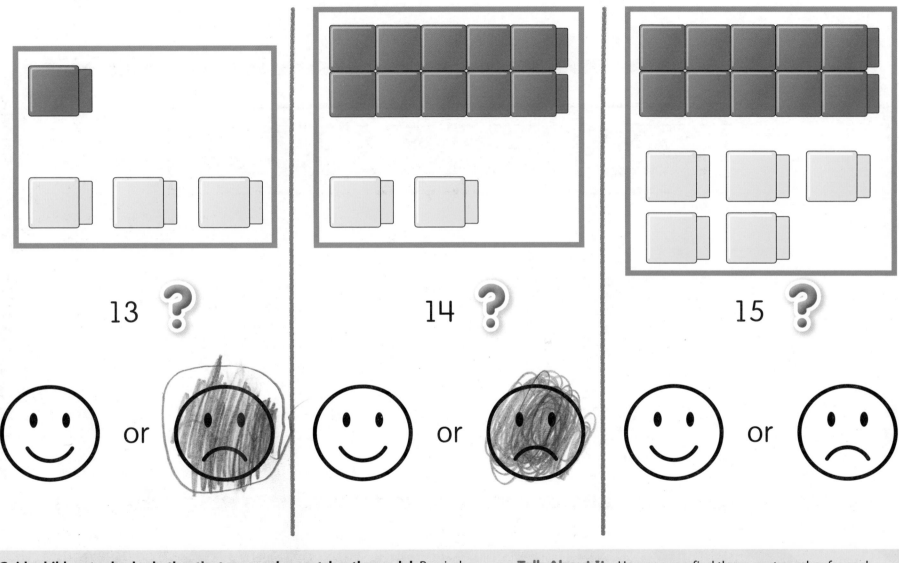

Name _____

13 ❓

😊 or ☹️

14 ❓

😊 or ☹️

15 ❓

😊 or ☹️

Guide children to check whether the teen number matches the model. Remind them that teen numbers are 10 and some more. Have children color the happy face if the number shown is correct or the sad face if it is wrong.

Talk About It How can you find the correct number for each picture?

Count Teen Numbers

Show 16.

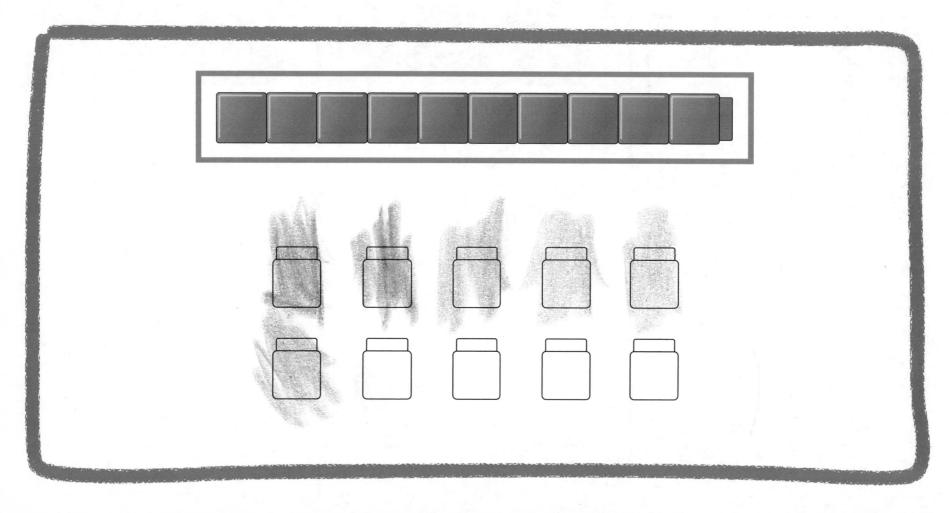

Have children color cubes below the group of 10 cubes to show 16 cubes altogether. Children can color any 6 cubes. When children are finished, have them hold up their work to share different solutions.

<u>**Talk About It**</u> What would you do differently if you were asked to show 17?

Count Teen Numbers

Children build and count a group of 15 objects and read the corresponding number. Say: *We need to make 3 relay teams. 5 children are on each team. How many children do we need?* Arrange 3 groups of 5 children in a 3 × 5 array.

Together, count each child, one at a time. Then have children count the squares. Ask children to circle 2 groups of 5 and say how many are in the circled group. Ask children to count the number of squares again, starting from 10.

Children build and count groups of objects from 11 to 20. Have children place 10 counters in the top 10-frame. Guide children to recognize this as a group of 10. Have children place 1 counter in the bottom 10-frame.

Ask: *How many?* Display the number card for 11. Children continue adding 1 counter at a time to the bottom 10-frame and counting until there are 20 counters. Display the corresponding number card each time.

Count Teen Numbers

Name _____

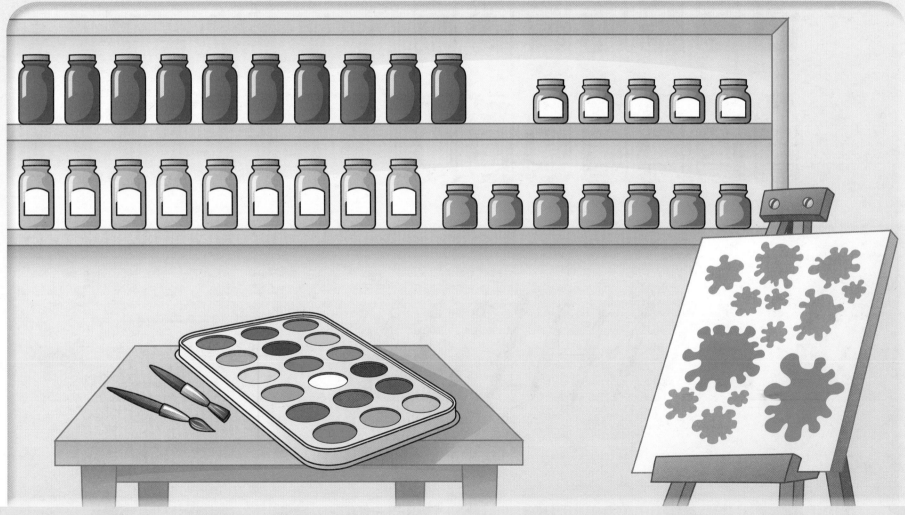

Ask children to describe the quantities they see in the picture. Together count the 10 blue paint jars, then find how many jars on the top shelf, how many tall jars, and how many jars without a label. Have children find and circle a group of 18.

<u>Talk About It</u> How can you keep track of which things you have counted?

Count Teen Numbers

12

13 - - - - - -

14

12

13 - - - - - -

14

Guide children to count teen numbers. Have children count the number of each object. Then have them write the number they counted. Have children check their answer by circling a group of 10 objects and then counting the "extras."

<u>Talk About It</u>   How many "extras" do you have in each problem? Where do you see the number of extras in the teen number?

Count Teen Numbers

Name _____

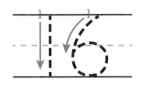 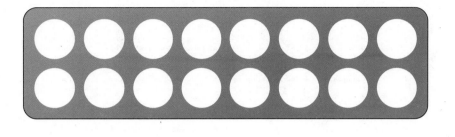

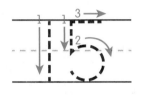 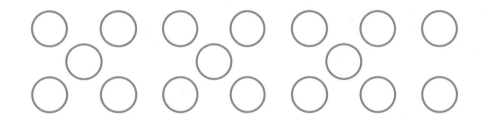

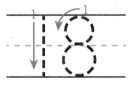

Guide children to trace each teen number and then count out that number of objects. Guide children to lightly mark each object as they count to keep track of what they have counted. Have children count again, coloring the objects as they go.

<u>Talk About It</u> Work with a partner. Did you both color the same shapes in each picture? Does it matter which shapes you color?

Count Teen Numbers

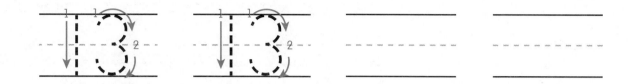

Draw 13.

Have children trace and write 13 and then draw 13 objects. Tell children to trace and write the number 13. Have children draw 13 objects. You may want to suggest objects that are easy for children to draw, such as circles or happy faces.

Talk About It How did you know when to stop drawing? How would your picture be different if you were asked to draw 14?

Make Teen Numbers

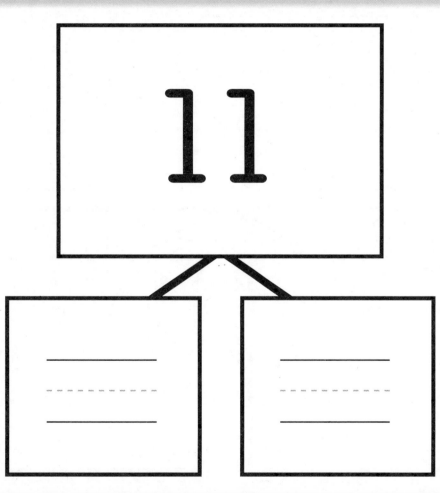

Children form groups of 10 and some extra and represent teen numbers in a number bond. Have children act out 11 by having 10 children stand in a group and 1 child to the side. Say: *11 is 10 and 1 more.* Repeat for 12 to 19.

Then write 11 in a number bond as 10 and 1 on the board. Have children complete the number bond for 11. Then write 10 + 1 = 11 on the board and relate it to the number bond.

Make Teen Numbers

Children represent teen numbers 12 to 19 in a number bond. Write the number bond for 12 as 10 and 2 on the board. Have children use number cards to show 12 as 10 and 2 in the number bond. Together, say: *12 is 10 and 2 more.*

Write 10 + 2 = 12 on the board next to the number bond. Guide children to see how the number bond and equation are related. Repeat for the numbers 13 to 19.

Explore Together
Make Teen Numbers

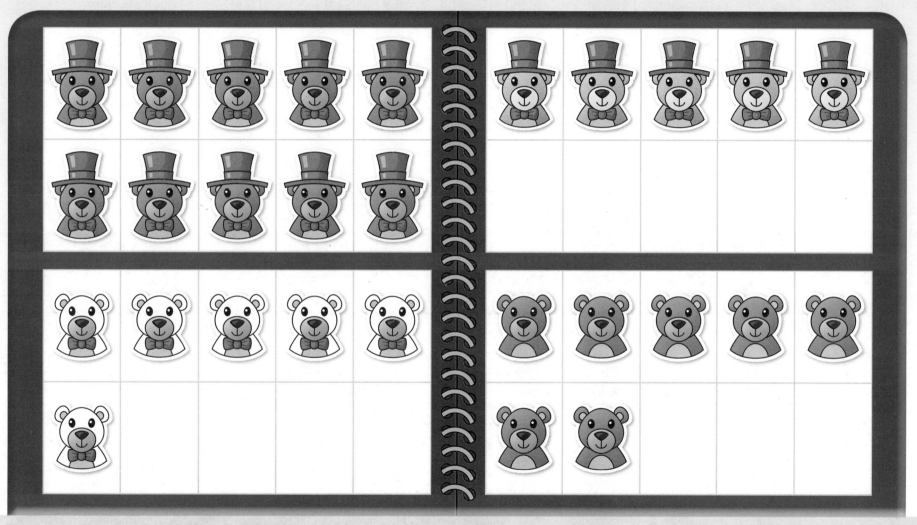

Encourage children to count the number of brown bears, bears with bows, and bears with hats. Identify the number in each group as 10 with some extras. Have children draw a brown bear in the bottom right and tell how many brown bears there are now.

<u>Talk About It</u> Are there more bears with bows or more bears with hats? How do you know?

Practice Together
Make Teen Numbers

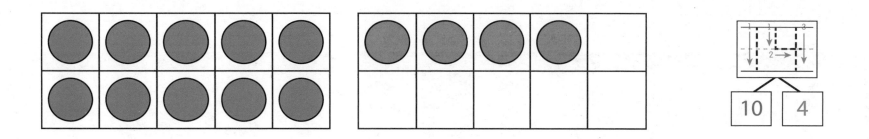

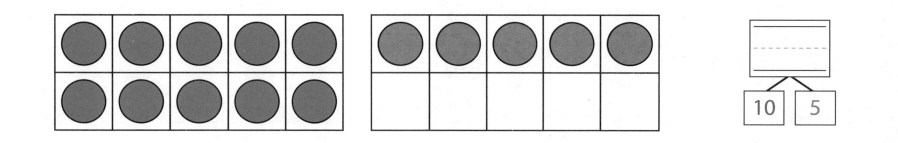

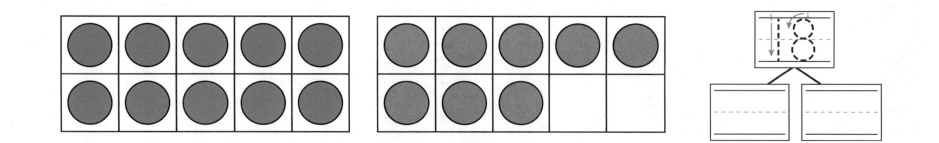

Guide children to use 10-frames and number bonds to show teen numbers. Have children write the total number of counters at the top of the number bond and the number of red and blue counters below. Express the number as 10 with some extras.

<u>Talk About It</u> What are some things that are the same in every problem? Why do you think those things are the same?

Practice Together
Make Teen Numbers

Name _____

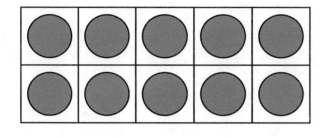 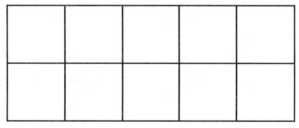 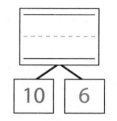

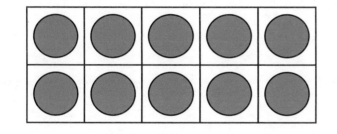 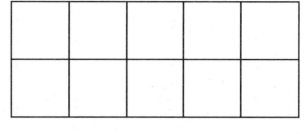 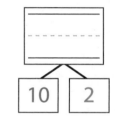

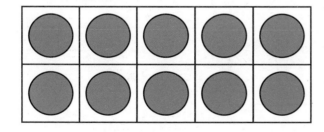 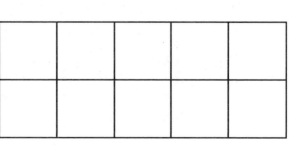 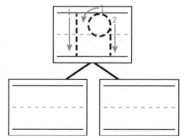

Make Teen Numbers

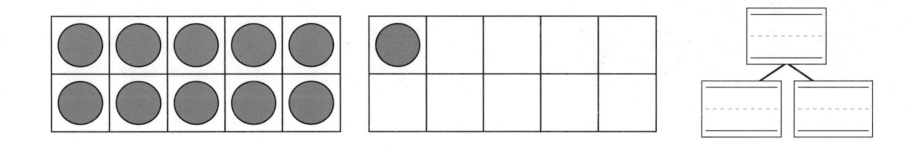

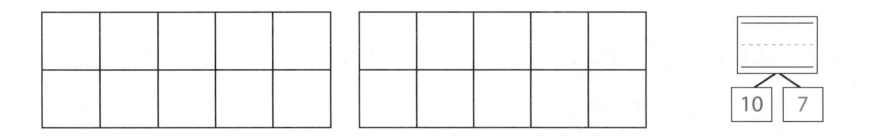

Have children complete 10-frames and number bonds to model teen numbers. In the first problem, have children use the 10-frame to complete the number bond. In the last problem, tell children to draw counters to match the number bond, then write the total.

<u>**Talk About It**</u> Which problem was easier for you? Why?

©Curriculum Associates, LLC   Copying is not permitted.

Count to 100 by Tens

Children build a 100-cube train from 10-cube trains, and compare its length to the height of a doorway. Place a piece of tape the length of a classroom doorway on the floor. Have each child build a 10-cube train.

Invite 10 children to place their trains alongside the doorway tape. As each train is added, count the cubes by tens. Children compare the length of the 100-cube train to the height of the doorway. Discuss results.

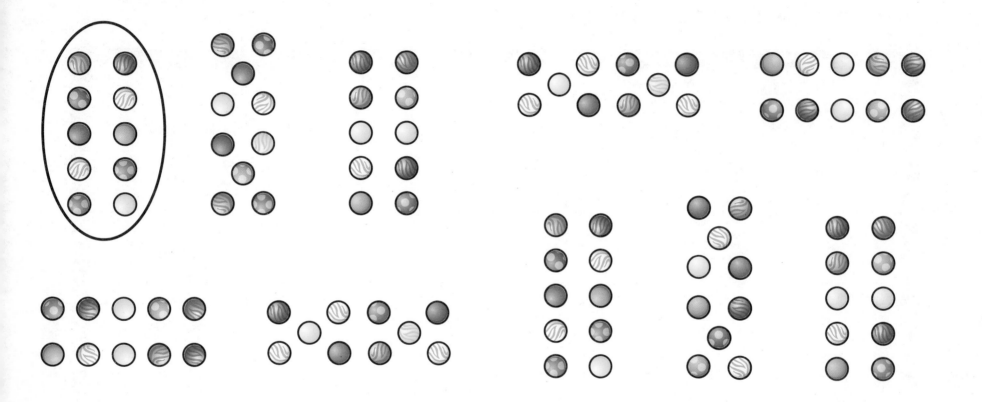

Children use fingers to show groups of ten, and then count to 100 by tens. Have 1 child show a group of 10 fingers to the class. Invite 9 more children to do the same. As a class, count the fingers by tens. Then identify the circled marbles as a group of ten. Have children circle all the groups of 10. Ask: *How many marbles do you think there are in all*? Count by tens aloud together as children point to each group of marbles.

Count to 100 by Tens

Name _____

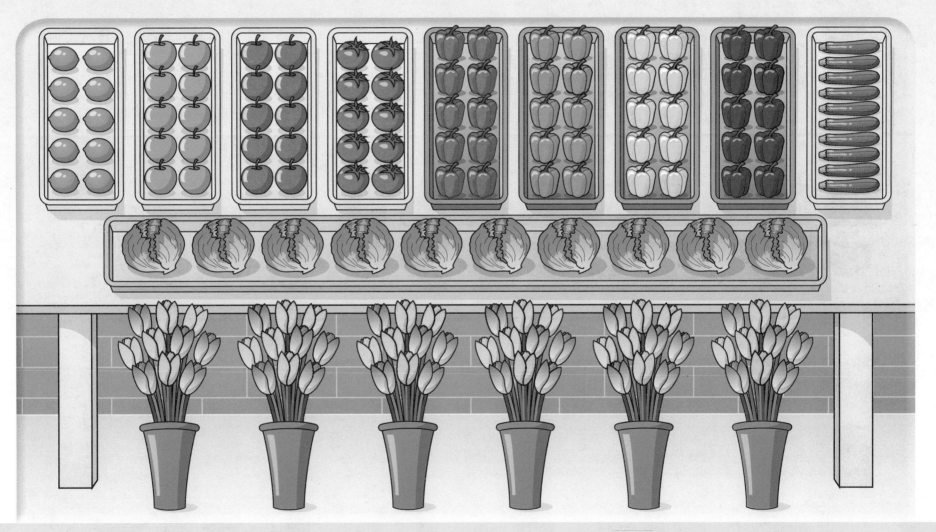

Encourage children to count different groups of objects by tens. Tell children each basket and flower pot has 10 objects in it. Then count the groups of objects, such as all the green food items, by tens. Have children circle 40 flowers.

<u>Talk About It</u> How does knowing how to count to 10 help you count by tens?

Count to 100 by Tens

50   60   70

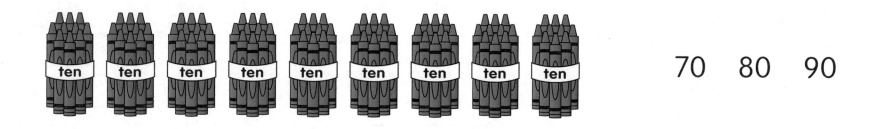

70   80   90

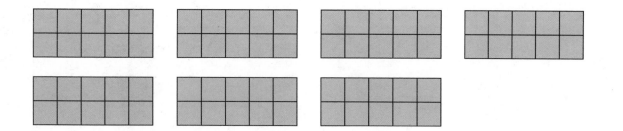

60   70   80

Guide children to count objects by tens. Explain that there are 10 objects in each group. Count the number of objects in each problem aloud by tens. Have children circle the total number.

Talk About It   Which do you think is easier: counting each square or counting the squares by tens? Why?

Count to 100 by Tens

Name _____

1	2	3	4	5	6	7	8	9	
11	12	13	14	15	16	17	18	19	20
21	22	23	24	25	26	27	28	29	30
31	32	33	34	35	36	37	38	39	
41	42	43	44	45	46	47	48	49	
51	52	53	54	55	56	57	58	59	60
61	62	63	64	65	66	67	68	69	70
71	72	73	74	75	76	77	78	79	
81	82	83	84	85	86	87	88	89	90
91	92	93	94	95	96	97	98	99	

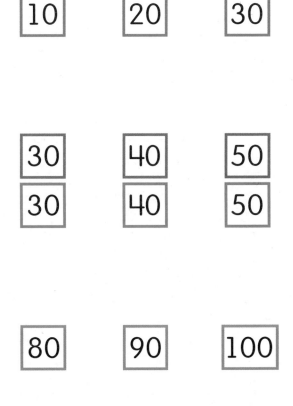

| 10 | 20 | 30 |

| 30 | 40 | 50 |
| 30 | 40 | 50 |

| 80 | 90 | 100 |

| 80 | 90 | 100 |

Guide children to circle the numbers that complete the hundreds chart. Count aloud to 10 by ones to solve the first problem. Then guide children to focus on the last column and count together by tens to complete the page.

<u>Talk About It</u> What do you notice about all the tens numbers?

Count to 100 by Tens

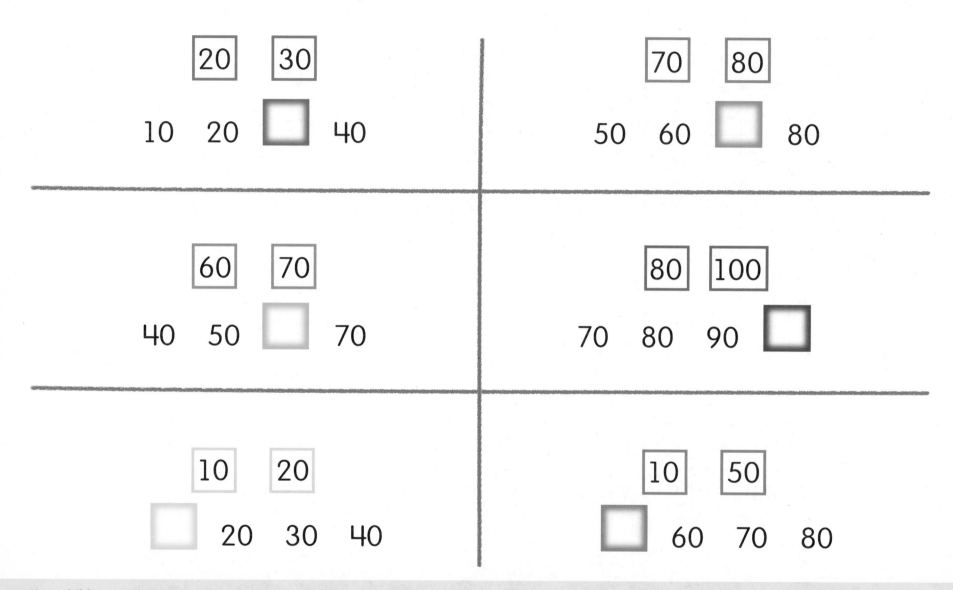

| 20 | 30 |
| 10 | 20 | ☐ | 40 |

| 70 | 80 |
| 50 | 60 | ☐ | 80 |

| 60 | 70 |
| 40 | 50 | ☐ | 70 |

| 80 | 100 |
| 70 | 80 | 90 | ☐ |

| 10 | 20 |
| ☐ | 20 | 30 | 40 |

| 10 | 50 |
| ☐ | 60 | 70 | 80 |

Have children circle the number to complete each list. The problems in the bottom row ask for the first number in the list. Allow children to struggle. Provide time for them to try strategies on their own. They may realize they can try each number to see which one "sounds right."

Talk About It How did you decide which number to circle?

Count to 100 by Ones

			March			
Sunday	**Monday**	**Tuesday**	**Wednesday**	**Thursday**	**Friday**	**Saturday**
1	2	3	4	5	6	7
8	9	10	11	12	13	14
15	16	17	18	19	20	21
22	23	24	25	26	27	28
29	30	31				

Children review counting to 31 using a calendar. Say: *A calendar is a chart that shows numbers in order. We use the calendar to count the days in each month.*

Have children point to the dates in order and lead the class in saying each number aloud together.

1	2	3	4	5	6	7	8	9	10
11	12	13	14	15	16	17	18	19	20
21	22	23	24	25	26	27	28	29	30
31	32	33	34	35	36	37	38	39	40
41	42	43	44	45	46	47	48	49	50
51	52	53	54	55	56	57	58	59	60
61	62	63	64	65	66	67	68	69	70
71	72	73	74	75	76	77	78	79	80
81	82	83	84	85	86	87	88	89	90
91	92	93	94	95	96	97	98	99	100

Children count to 100 using a hundreds chart and in a circle. Introduce the hundreds chart. Say: *A hundreds chart is another chart that shows numbers in order.* Have children point to each number and say the number out loud as the class counts to 100 together. Repeat the counting several times. Then have children form a circle and count to 100 together while passing an object around the circle.

Count to 100 by Ones

Name _____

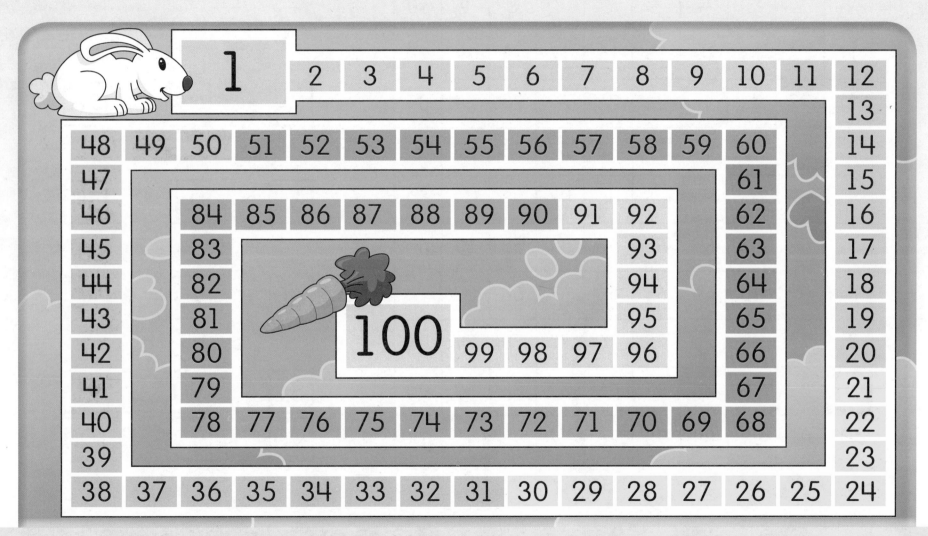

Encourage children to count by ones to 100 to help the bunny count his steps until he gets to the carrot. Tell children to use their fingers to keep track. Guide children to circle all the numbers you say when you count by tens.

<u>Talk About It</u> How does knowing how to count from 1 to 10 help you count to 100?

Count to 100 by Ones

1	2	3	4	5	6	7	8	9	10
11	12	13	14	15	16	17	18	19	20
21	22	23		25	26	27	28	29	30
31	32	33	34	35	36	37	38	39	40
41	42	43		45	46	47	48	49	50
51	52	53	54	55	56	57	58	59	60
61	62	63	64	65	66	67	68	69	
71	72	73	74	75	76	77	78	79	80
	82	83	84	85	86	87	88	89	90
91	92	93	94	95	96	97	98		100

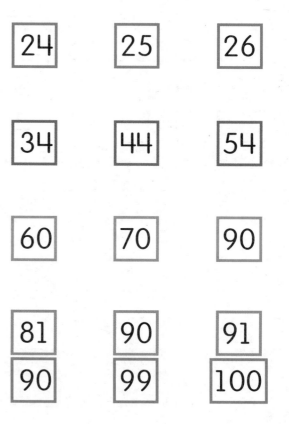

24	25	26
34	44	54
60	70	90
81 / 90	90 / 99	91 / 100

Guide children to circle the numbers that complete the hundreds chart. Count aloud by ones until you get to the first white box. Together determine the missing number and which one to circle. Count on together from 24 until you reach the next box, and so on.

<u>**Talk About It**</u> What patterns can you find in the hundreds chart?

Count to 100 by Ones

Name _____

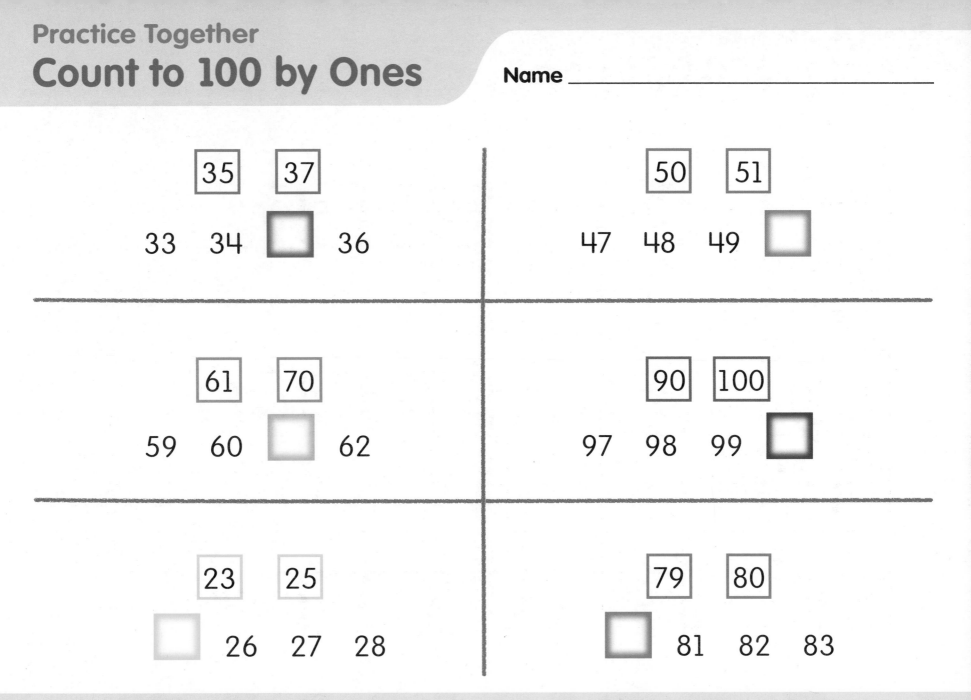

35	37			50	51	

33   34   ☐   36

47   48   49   ☐

| 61 | 70 | | | 90 | 100 | |

59   60   ☐   62

97   98   99   ☐

| 23 | 25 | | | 79 | 80 | |

☐   26   27   28

☐   81   82   83

Guide children to circle the correct number to complete each list. Read the list of numbers aloud, and discuss. Allow the class time to work out a strategy for determining the correct choice.

Talk About It   How did you decide which number to circle?

Count to 100 by Ones

| 20 | 21 | 22 | 32 | 24 | 25 | 26 |

| 57 | 58 | 59 | 59 | 61 | 62 | 63 |

| 74 | 75 | 76 | 77 | 78 | 79 | 88 |

Have children cross out the box that shows the incorrect number in the number path.
Read each list of numbers aloud and have children independently decide which number does not belong. Check answers as a class, asking children to say the correct number.

<u>Talk About It</u> How did you decide which numbers were wrong?

Compare Length

Children identify attributes of shoes and make comparison statements based on length. Display two shoes of different sizes. Invite children to describe the two shoes. Model a comparison statement, such as: *The blue shoe is longer than the white shoe*. Have children make comparison statements using *shorter, heavier,* and *lighter*. Have children make comparison statements about the shoes shown and circle the one that is longer.

Children compare lengths of pencils and make comparison statements.
Give pairs 2 pencils of different lengths. Have children compare the length of each pencil to the pencil shown. Guide them to describe each pencil in relation to the picture of the pencil using *shorter* or *longer*.

Compare Length

Name _____

Encourage children to compare objects based on their heights or lengths. Model statements, such as: *The yellow bat is longer than the red bat.* Have children circle the taller or longer object for each comparison.

<u>**Talk About It**</u> How can you tell which of the 3 boats is the longest?

Compare Length

Guide children to identify which objects are taller or longer, and which objects are shorter. Have children circle the shorter object in each pair. Ask children to explain why the object is shorter than the other object.

<u>Talk About It</u> How did you decide which bat is shorter?

Compare Length

Name _____

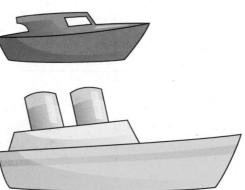

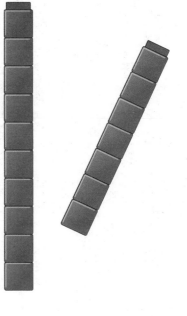

Guide children to identify which objects are taller or longer, and which objects are shorter. Have children circle the taller or longer object in each pair. Ask children to explain how they decided which object is taller or longer.

<u>Talk About It</u> How could you be sure which group of cubes is longer?

Compare Length

Have children draw pictures to show *taller* and *shorter*. Have children draw a flower that is taller and a bat that is shorter than those shown. After completing the page, have children describe how they decided how to draw the items.

<u>**Talk About It**</u> How would you draw a flower that is not shorter than and not taller than the flower shown?

Compare Weight

Children identify and describe measurable attributes of objects and then describe their weights. Display a bag of flour. Ask: *How can you describe the size of this object?* Explain that *weight* is the word for how heavy or light an object is. Invite children to hold the flour, describe it as *heavy* or *light*, and explain why. Repeat with the other objects. Have children circle the heavy objects and cross out the light objects.

Encourage children to describe objects based on their weight. Encourage statements such as: *The jug of milk is heavier than the juice box*. Have children circle three objects that are lighter than a gallon of milk.

<u>Talk About It</u> How did you decide which items are lighter than the gallon of milk?

Guide children to identify which objects are heavier. Have children circle the heavier object in each pair. Ask children to explain how they know that the object they circled is heavier than the other object.

<u>Talk About It</u> How did you decide which object is heavier?

Practice Together
Compare Weight

Name _____

Guide children to identify which objects are lighter. Have children circle the lighter object. Ask children to explain how they decided which object is lighter.

<u>Talk About It</u>   Is the smaller object always lighter? Give an example to support your answer.

Have children draw pictures to show one object that is heavier than an empty backpack and one object that is lighter than an empty backpack. After children draw their pictures, have them circle the heavier object in red and the lighter one in blue.

<u>**Talk About It**</u> Can you think of an object that is smaller than an empty backpack, but is heavier?

Sort Objects

Children sort books, then count and compare the number in each group.
Have children sort books into groups by size and count to find the total in each group. Write the totals on the board and have children record. As a class, compare the numbers using language such as *more than*, *fewer than*, *the same as*, and *equal*. Repeat, having the class sort the books another way.

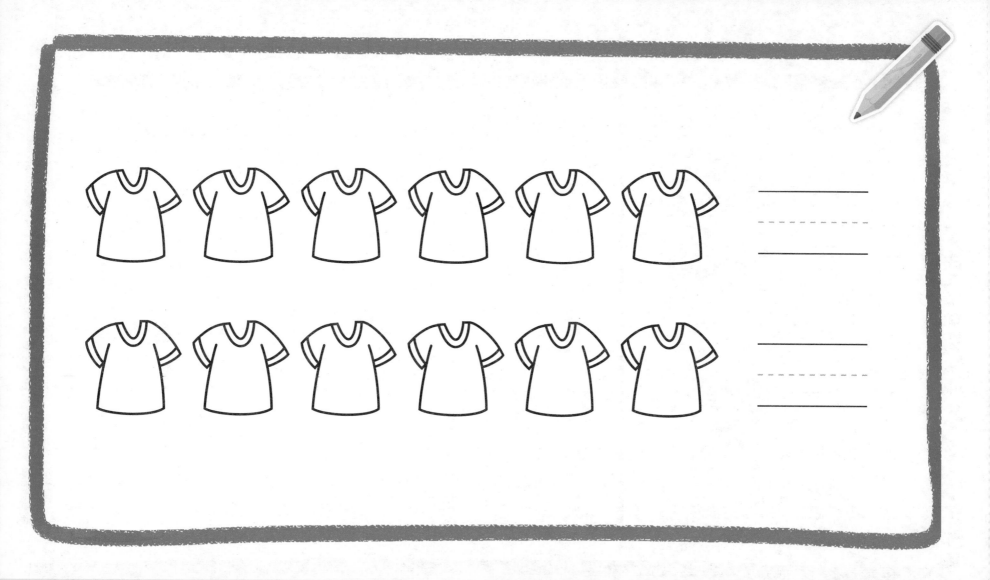

Children determine the categories used to sort. Invite 5 children in dark-colored tops and 6 in light-colored tops to the front. Have children identify the categories used to sort and find the total in each group.

Children color the top row of shirts to show the number in the dark-colored top group and the bottom row to show the number in the light-colored top group. Then children write the total and compare the numbers.

Encourage children to sort objects based on color, size, or feature. Ask probing questions, such as: *How many bubbles are big? How many are small?* Have children circle the striped fish and then count the number of striped and not-striped fish.

<u>Talk About It</u> Describe two different ways you could sort the rocks.

Guide children to identify one object that does not belong with the others. Explain that there is more than one correct answer. Have children cross out one object they see as different. Have children share their answers and the reasons for each.

<u>**Talk About It**</u> How did you decide which object to cross out?

Sort Objects

Name _____

Guide children to sort the objects. Guide children to realize that the two given groups are heavy objects and light objects. Have children circle the objects at the bottom of the page with a blue or green crayon to show which group they belong to.

<u>Talk About It</u> What are some other objects that could go in the blue box? How do you decide?

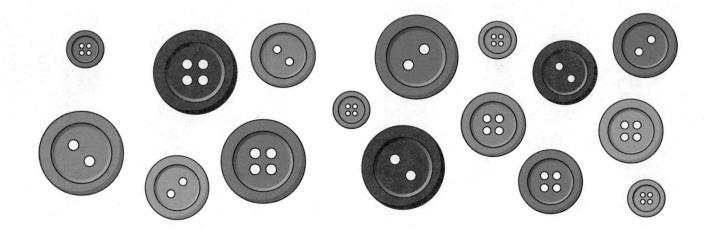

Have children sort the buttons by color. Have children count the number of buttons of each color and write the number in the box of the same color. Have children compare the number of buttons in the red group to the number in each of the other groups.

<u>Talk About It</u> What is another way you could sort these buttons?

See Position and Shape

Children are introduced to position words and place objects in different positions. Introduce position words by pointing to different objects in the room and describing them as *above, below, beside, in front of, behind,* or *next to* another object. Ask children to use position words to describe the position of one child relative to another child. Then have children place an object in a position as described relative to Snargg.

Children draw pictures positioned as described relative to the camper and act out position words. Have children draw pictures positioned relative to the camper as described. Say: *Draw a star below the camper.* Then they play *Teacher Says,* a variation of *Simon Says,* as a class to act out positions. Say: *Teacher says, place your hand above your head.* Occasionally omit the phrase *Teacher says* before the instruction.

Explore Together
See Position and Shape

Name <u>Yasin</u>

Encourage children to describe shapes and the position of objects. Guide children to use words such as *above, below, beside, in front of, behind,* and *next to.* Have children ring (circle) an object next to the dog.

<u>**Talk About It**</u> What shapes do you see in the picture?

See Position and Shape

Guide children to identify objects that are below, beside, behind, or above. Have children circle the pictures where the leaf is below the can and the ball is behind the dog. Then have them circle the person beside the dog and the object above the bus.

<u>Talk About It</u> What are some other ways you can describe the objects in these pictures?

172 **Lesson 29 • Guided Practice**

See Position and Shape

Name _____

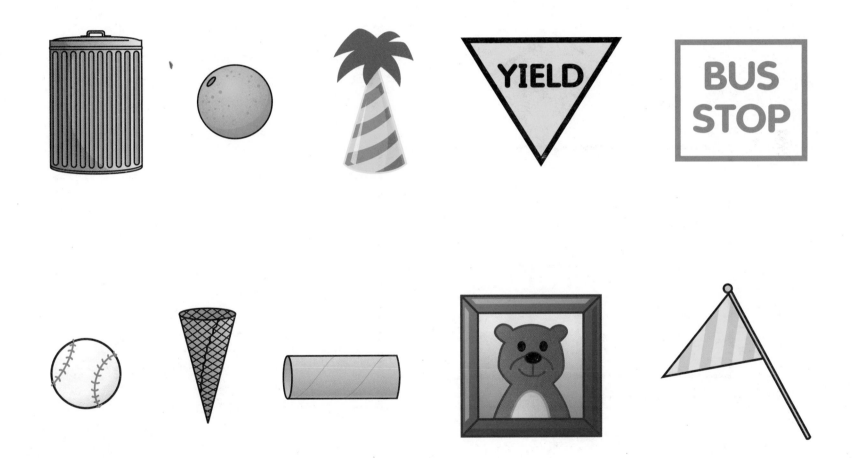

Guide children to match the shapes with the same name. Have children draw lines to connect the objects with the same shape and then name the shape. Use real objects to help children recognize that orientation or size do not change the name used to describe the shape.

<u>Talk About It</u> Work with a partner. How did you decide which objects match?

See Position and Shape

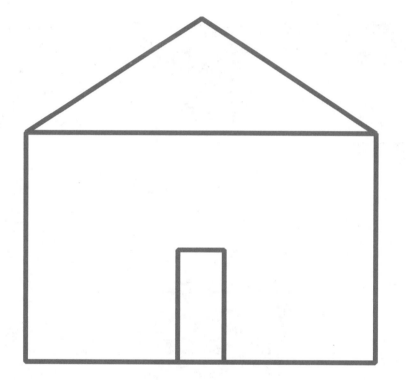

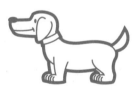

Have children draw shapes and objects from verbal instructions. Have children draw: a cloud above the house, a flower in front of the house, a boy next to the house, a window beside the door, a circle above the door, a rock below the window, and a tree behind the dog.

<u>Talk About It</u> Work with a partner. Are the locations of the objects in your drawings the same? How are they different?

Name _____

Name Shapes

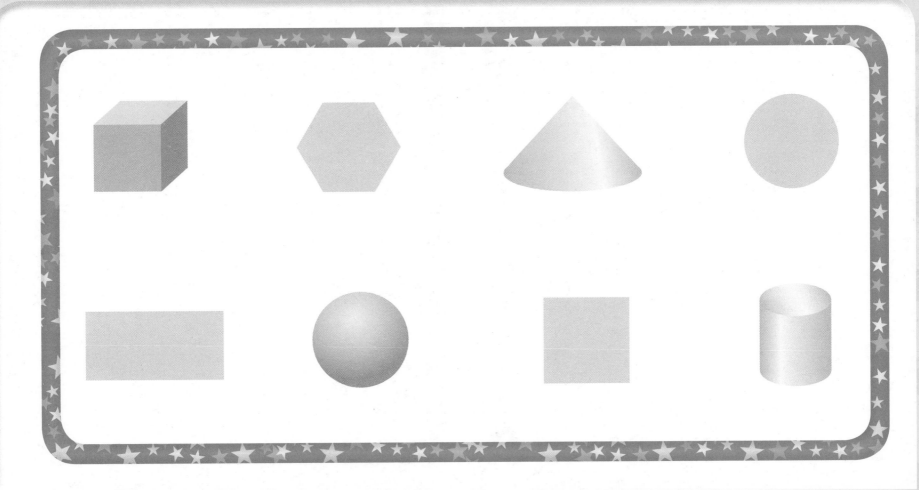

Children differentiate solid shapes from flat shapes and informally describe shapes. Display a circle, square, triangle, rectangle, hexagon, cube, cone, cylinder, and sphere. For each shape, name the shape and have children repeat it. Then have children informally describe each shape, including if it is flat or solid. Then name a shape and have children point to that shape above and tell if it is solid or flat.

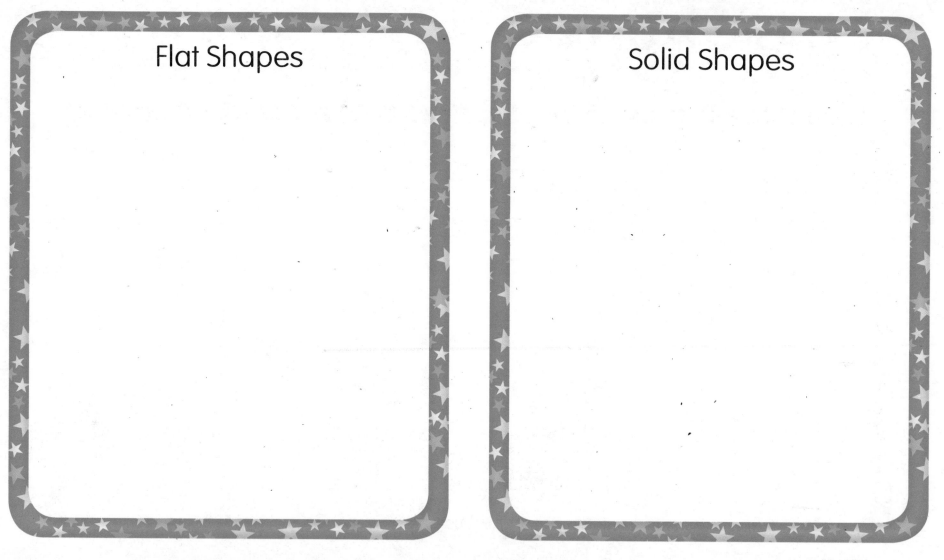

Flat Shapes

Solid Shapes

Children identify shapes as flat or solid and name the shapes. Have pairs of children sort flat shape and solid shape cards and then name each of the shapes. Children then use a flat hand or a fist to identify objects they are shown as flat or solid.

Explore Together
Name Shapes

Name _____

Encourage children to describe the two- and three-dimensional shapes in the picture including squares, rectangles, circles, triangles, hexagons, spheres, cubes, cones, and cylinders. Have children ring (circle) one example of each solid.

Talk About It What shapes are the easiest to find? Which shapes are the most difficult to find?

Name Shapes

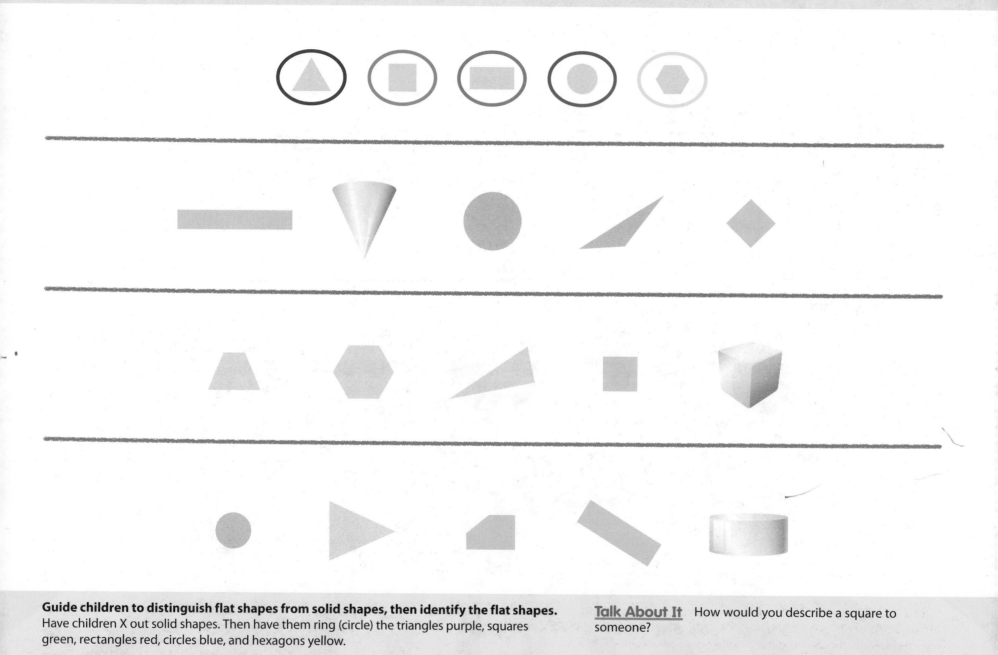

Guide children to distinguish flat shapes from solid shapes, then identify the flat shapes.
Have children X out solid shapes. Then have them ring (circle) the triangles purple, squares green, rectangles red, circles blue, and hexagons yellow.

<u>Talk About It</u> How would you describe a square to someone?

Name Shapes

Name _____

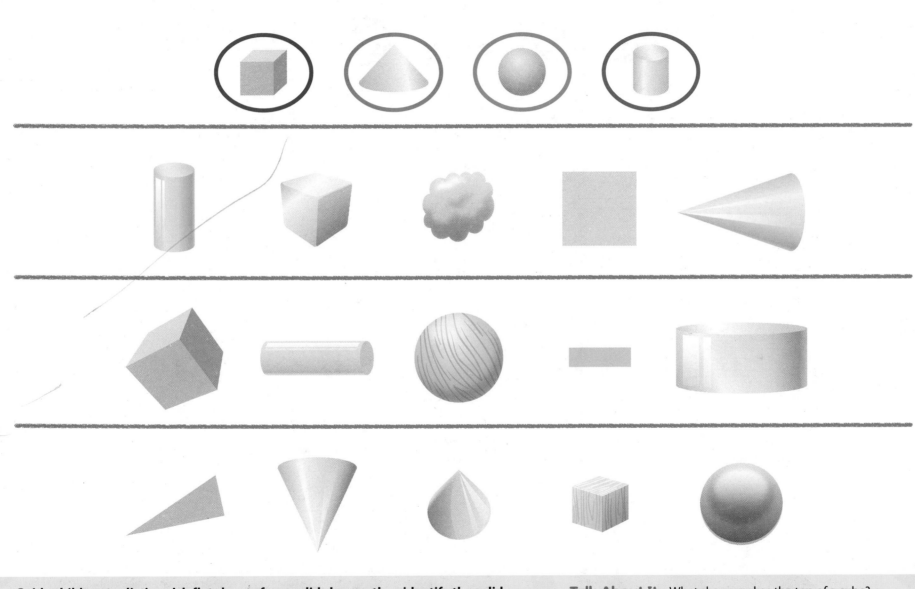

Guide children to distinguish flat shapes from solid shapes, then identify the solid shapes. Have children X out flat shapes. Then have them ring (circle) the cubes purple, cones red, spheres green, and cylinders blue.

<u>**Talk About It**</u> What shape makes the top of a cube?

Practice by Myself
Name Shapes

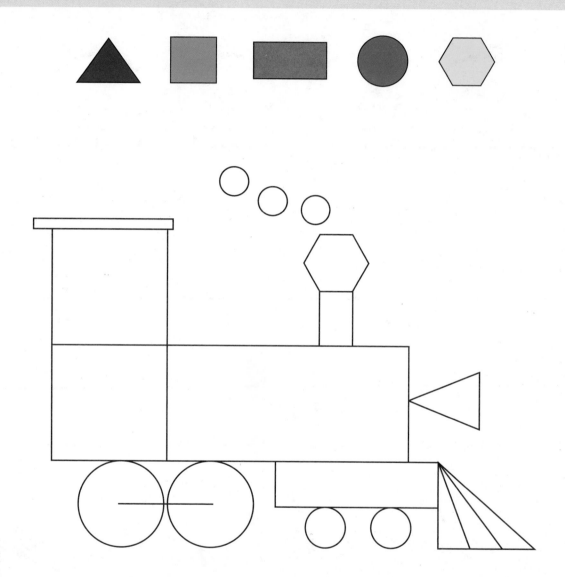

Have children color the shapes in the picture using the colors at the top of the page.
Remind children to look for different kinds of rectangles and triangles.

Talk About It How many of each shape did you find?

Name _____

Compare Shapes

Children play a game to identify features that shapes have in common.
Give each child a flat or solid shape. Hold up a cube. Describe a feature of the cube and have children raise their hand if their shape has that feature.

Choose a child to identify the attribute on his or her shape. Then that child describes a different attribute. Repeat with other children. Then have children sort a cube, cylinder, circle, and square based on attributes you describe.

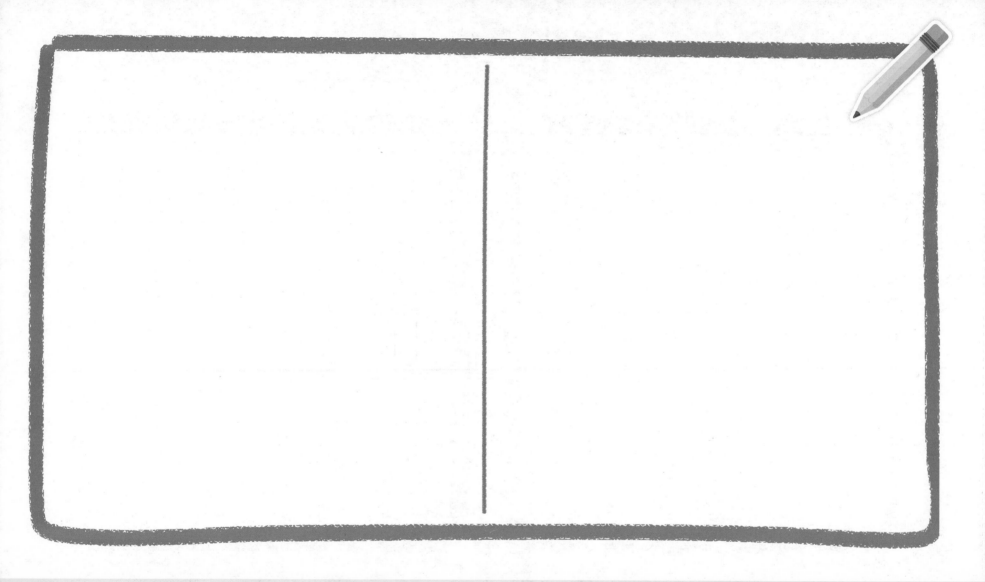

Children draw shapes with given attributes. Describe an attribute such as: *The shape is flat*. Have children hold up a shape that has that attribute. Then children discuss if more than one shape fits the description. Say: *The shape has no straight sides*. Have children draw a shape that fits this description on the left workmat. Say: *The shape has at least 3 sides*. Have children draw a shape that fits that description in the right workmat.

Encourage children to look for shapes that are alike in some way, and to describe how they are alike. Encourage children to talk about curves, corners, or the number or length of sides. Have children ring (circle) all the solid shapes that could roll on their own down a hill.

<u>Talk About It</u> What objects can you see in your classroom that have a shape like the shape of the paint cans?

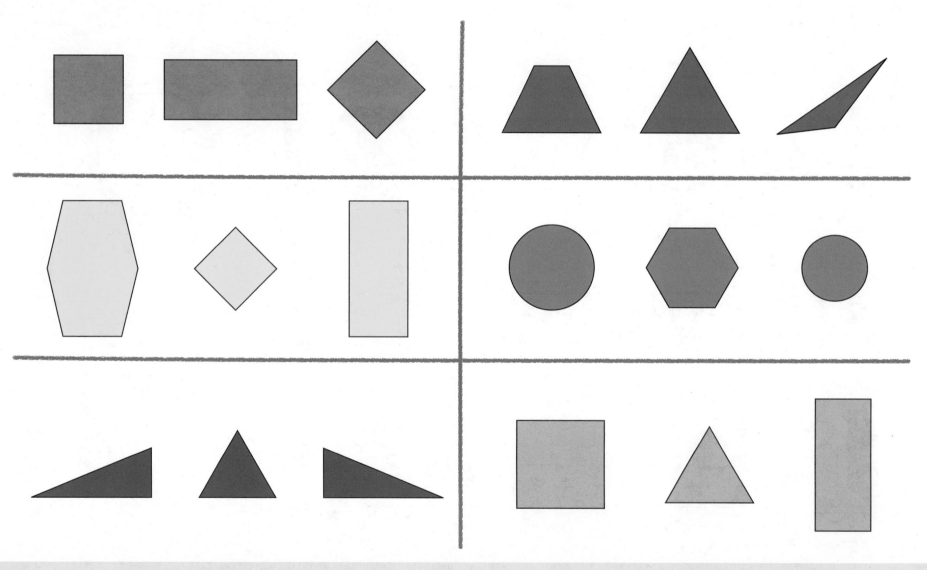

Guide children to ring (circle) the two shapes that are most alike. Have children focus their attention on the number of sides, the types of corners, or sides that are the same length. Guide children to describe both what is alike and what is different.

<u>Talk About It</u> Which shapes on the page are different from all the others? Describe how they are different.

Name _____

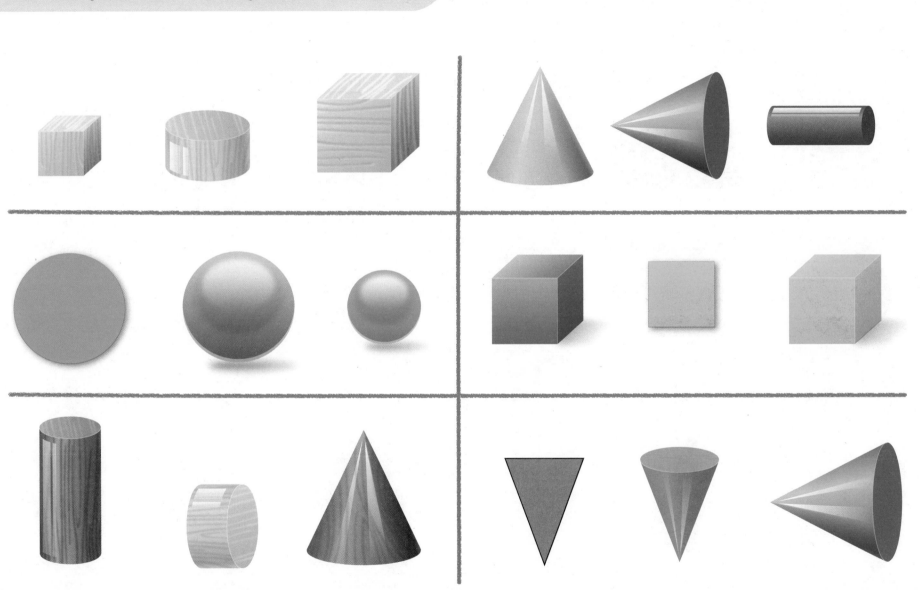

Guide children to ring (circle) the two shapes that are most alike. Have children focus their attention on whether the shapes are flat or solid, and what kind of solid. Guide children to describe both what is alike and what is different.

<u>Talk About It</u>   For each group, describe how the shape you did not ring is different from the other two shapes.

4 sides

☐ face

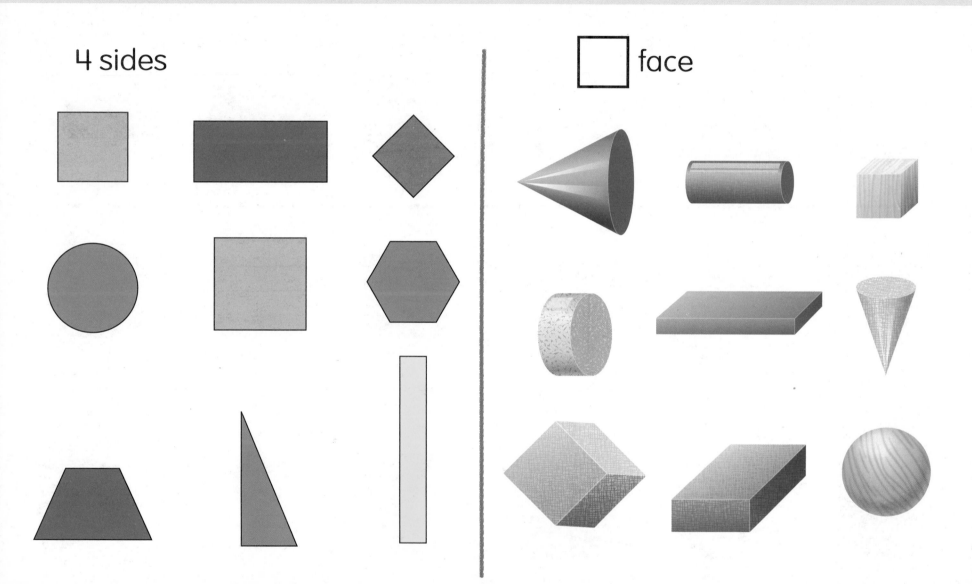

Have children analyze the flat shapes and solids and look for those with the given characteristic. On the left, have children ring (circle) figures with four sides. On the right, have children ring (circle) solids with a square face.

<u>Talk About It</u> How did you decide which shapes to ring?

Name _____

Build Shapes

Children put together shapes to make squares and rectangles. Give children 4 right triangles and 4 squares. Ask: _Which shapes can you put together to make a square?_ Have children arrange shapes in the workmat to make a square. Invite children to share how they combined shapes. Repeat, asking: _Which shapes can you use to make a rectangle?_ Repeat, asking: _How can you use triangles to make a rectangle?_

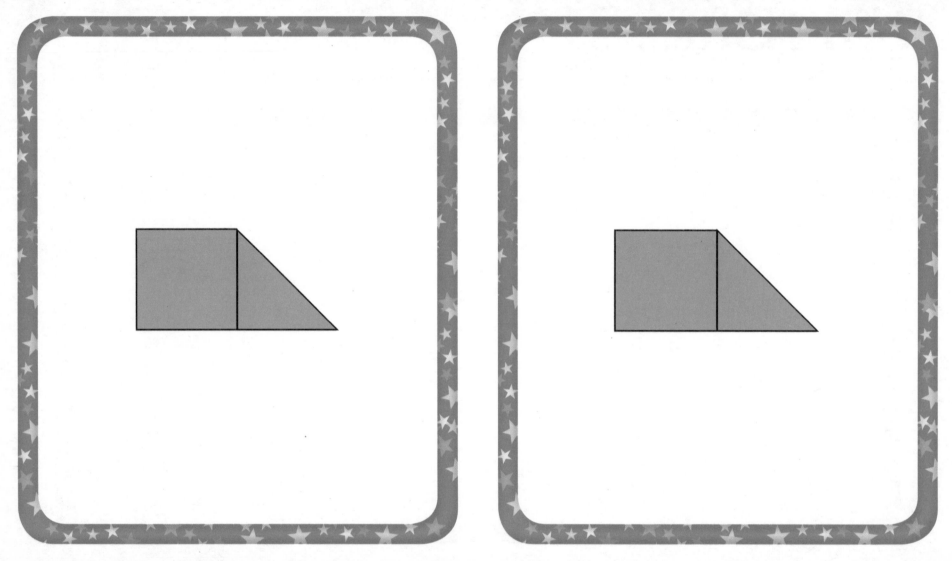

Children add shapes to an existing shape to make a rectangle and then a triangle. Ask: *How can I add another shape to make this shape a rectangle?* Have children add 1 shape to the shape to make a rectangle. Invite children to explain how to make a rectangle. Have children remove their shape and ask: *How can I add another shape to make this shape a triangle?* Have children add 1 shape to make a triangle and explain how.

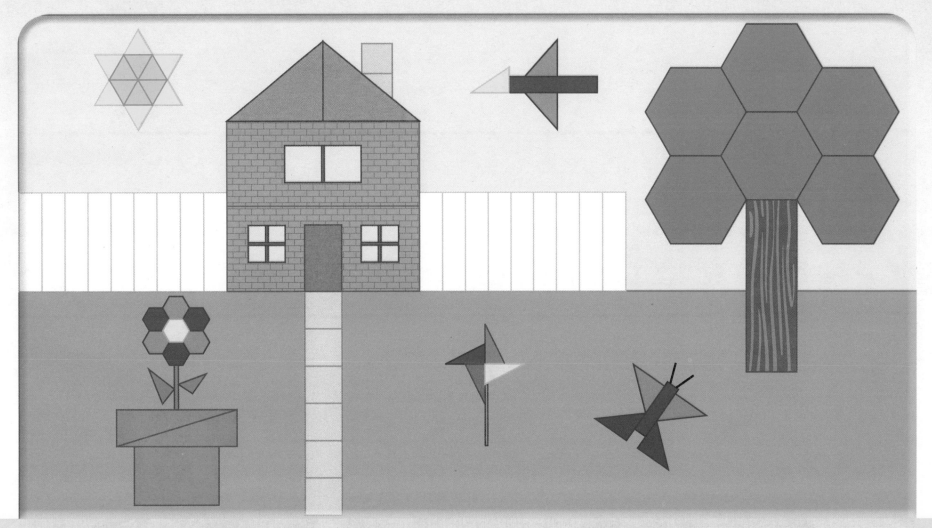

Encourage children to identify small shapes within bigger shapes. Guide children to find several examples, such as the small rectangles in the fence that make up the larger rectangle. Have children find and ring (circle) two squares that make a rectangle.

<u>Talk About It</u> What shape do you get when you put 2 squares together?

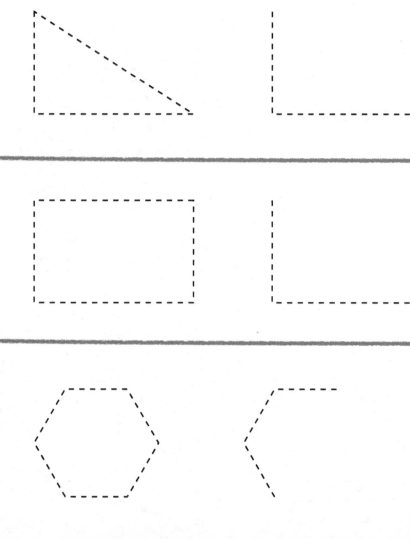

Guide children to trace a shape, complete a partial shape, and then draw another shape.
After tracing the first of each shape, discuss its features, such as number of sides and corners, and guide children to duplicate those features in their work.

<u>Talk About It</u>   What other ways can you draw a triangle?
What other ways can you draw a rectangle?

Build Shapes

Name _____

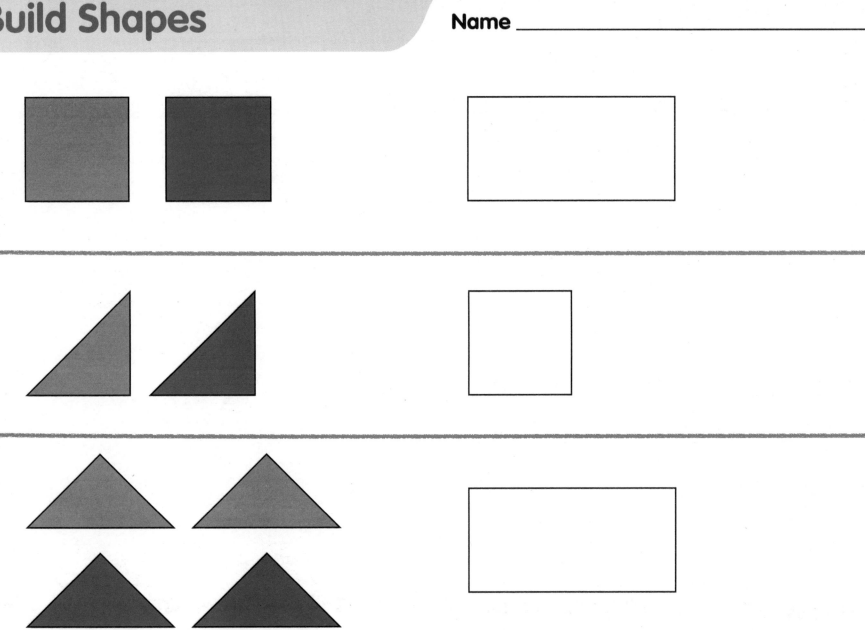

Guide children to use the colored shapes to make the outlined shape. Encourage children to use cutouts of the shapes to try different arrangements. Have children draw lines or color to show how the shapes fit into the outlined shape.

<u>Talk About It</u> What other shapes could you use to make the outlined shapes?

Build Shapes

Have children combine shapes to make a picture. Have children use the guide lines to color triangles and squares to make a picture or pattern of their own design.

<u>Talk About It</u> Work with a partner. How are your pictures alike? How are your pictures different?

Common Core State Standards Coverage by *Ready*® Instruction

The chart below correlates each Common Core State Standard to the *Ready*® *Instruction* lesson(s) that offer(s) comprehensive instruction on that standard. Use this chart to determine which lessons your students should complete based on their mastery of each standard.

Common Core State Standards for Grade K Mathematical Standards	Content Emphasis	*Ready*® Common Core Instruction Lesson(s)
Counting and Cardinality		
Know number names and the count sequence.		
K.CC.A.1 Count to 100 by ones and by tens.	Major	24, 25
K.CC.A.2 Count forward beginning from a given number within the known sequence (instead of having to begin at 1).	Major	24, 25
K.CC.A.3 Write numbers from 0 to 20. Represent a number of objects with a written numeral 0–20 (with 0 representing a count of no objects).	Major	2–4, 7, 9, 11, 22
Count to tell the number of objects.		
K.CC.B.4 Understand the relationship between numbers and quantities; connect counting to cardinality.		1–5, 7, 9, 11, 12
K.CC.B.4a When counting objects, say the number names in the standard order, pairing each object with one and only one number name and each number name with one and only one object.		1–4, 7, 9, 11
K.CC.B.4b Understand that the last number name said tells the number of objects counted. The number of objects is the same regardless of their arrangement or the order in which they were counted.	Major	1–4, 7, 9, 11
K.CC.B.4c Understand that each successive number name refers to a quantity that is one larger.		5, 12
K.CC.B.5 Count to answer "how many?" questions about as many as 20 things arranged in a line, a rectangular array, or a circle, or as many as 10 things in a scattered configuration; given a number from 1–20, count out that many objects.	Major	2–4, 7, 9, 11, 22
Compare numbers.		
K.CC.C.6 Identify whether the number of objects in one group is greater than, less than, or equal to the number of objects in another group, e.g., by using matching and counting strategies.	Major	5, 12
K.CC.C.7 Compare two numbers between 1 and 10 presented as written numerals.	Major	5, 12

Common Core State Standards for Grade K Mathematical Standards	Content Emphasis	*Ready*® Common Core Instruction Lesson(s)
Operations and Algebraic Thinking		
Understand addition as putting together and adding to, and understand subtraction as taking apart and taking from.		
K.OA.A.1 Represent addition and subtraction with objects, fingers, mental images, drawings, sounds (e.g., claps), acting out situations, verbal explanations, expressions, or equations.	Major	14, 16
K.OA.A.2 Solve addition and subtraction word problems, and add and subtract within 10, e.g., by using objects or drawings to represent the problem.	Major	15, 17–19
K.OA.A.3 Decompose numbers less than or equal to 10 into pairs in more than one way, e.g., by using objects or drawings, and record each decomposition by a drawing or equation (e.g., $5 = 2 + 3$ and $5 = 4 + 1$).	Major	6, 8, 10, 13
K.OA.A.4 For any number from 1 to 9, find the number that makes 10 when added to the given number, e.g., by using objects or drawings, and record the answer with a drawing or equation.	Major	13
K.OA.A.5 Fluently add and subtract within 5.	Major	15, 17, 20
Number and Operations in Base Ten		
Work with numbers 11–19 to gain foundations for place value.		
K.NBT.A.1 Compose and decompose numbers from 11 to 19 into ten ones and some further ones, e.g., by using objects or drawings, and record each composition or decomposition by a drawing or equation (such as $18 = 10 + 8$); understand that these numbers are composed of ten ones and one, two, three, four, five, six, seven, eight, or nine ones.	Major	21, 23
Measurement and Data		
Describe and compare measurable attributes.		
K.MD.A.1 Describe measurable attributes of objects, such as length or weight. Describe several measurable attributes of a single object.	Supporting/ Additional	26, 27
K.MD.A.2 Directly compare two objects with a measurable attribute in common, to see which object has "more of"/"less of" the attribute, and describe the difference. *For example, directly compare the heights of two children and describe one child as taller/shorter.*	Supporting/ Additional	26, 27

Common Core State Standards for Grade K Mathematical Standards	Content Emphasis	*Ready*® Common Core Instruction Lesson(s)
Measurement and Data (continued)		
Classify objects and count the number of objects in each category.		
K.MD.B.3 Classify objects into given categories; count the numbers of objects in each category and sort the categories by count.	Supporting/ Additional	28
Geometry		
Identify and describe shapes (squares, circles, triangles, rectangles, hexagons, cubes, cones, cylinders, and spheres).		
K.G.A.1 Describe objects in the environment using names of shapes, and describe the relative positions of these objects using terms such as *above, below, beside, in front of, behind,* and *next to*.	Supporting/ Additional	29
K.G.A.2 Correctly name shapes regardless of their orientations or overall size.	Supporting/ Additional	30
K.G.A.3 Identify shapes as two-dimensional (lying in a plane, "flat") or three-dimensional ("solid").	Supporting/ Additional	30
Analyze, compare, create, and compose shapes.		
K.G.B.4 Analyze and compare two- and three-dimensional shapes, in different sizes and orientations, using informal language to describe their similarities, differences, parts (e.g., number of sides and vertices/"corners") and other attributes (e.g., having sides of equal length).	Supporting/ Additional	31
K.G.B.5 Model shapes in the world by building shapes from components (e.g., sticks and clay balls) and drawing shapes.	Supporting/ Additional	32
K.G.B.6 Compose simple shapes to form larger shapes. *For example, "Can you join these two triangles with full sides touching to make a rectangle?"*	Supporting/ Additional	32

Acknowledgments

Illustration Credits

page 1: Rob McClurkan

page 2: Rob McClurkan

page 14: Rob McClurkan

page 109: Rob McClurkan

page 151: Rob McClurkan

page 157: Rob McClurkan

page 158: Rob McClurkan

All other illustrations by Sam Valentino

Emily